READING 4

VOYAGES

WORKTEXT

THIRD EDITION

Reading 4: Voyages Worktext
Third Edition

Writers
Eileen Berry, MA
Kelly A. Payne, MEd
Stephanie Suhr, MEd
Leah R. Thomas, MEd

Biblical Worldview
Brian Collins, PhD
Bryan Smith, PhD

Academic Oversight
Jeff Heath, EdD

Project Editors
Leigh Kosin
Suzanne Olson

Project Coordinator
Heather Chisholm

Design Coordinator
Duane Nichols

Cover & Book Designer
Drew Fields

Page Layout
Ashley Tisdale

Permissions
Sylvia Gass
Rita Mitchell
Kathleen Thompson
Carrie Walker

Art Director
Del Thompson

Illustrators
Michael Asire
Jim Brooks
Paula Cheadle
Meredith Dillman
Zach Franzen
Justin Gerard
Cory Godbey
Preston Gravely
Jordan Harbin
Tom La Padula
Cynthia Long
Sandy Mehus
Kathy Pflug
Karelyn Siegler
Lynda Slattery
Julie Speer
Gabhor Utomo
Courtney Wise

Photo Credits
Key: (t) top; (c) center; (b) bottom; (l) left; (r) right
30 © iStock.com/Henrik Jonsson; **47l** Christin Lola/Shutterstock.com; **47c** Kuttelvaserova Stuchelova/Shutterstock.com; **47r** © iStock.com/Diane Labombarbe; **64** Getty Images/iStockphoto/Thinkstock; **102** Diane Garcia/Shutterstock.com; **104** National Baseball Library; **105** © iStock.com/capecodphoto; **106** macondo/Shutterstock.com; **134** Terry Vine/MediaBakery; **143** *From Pioneer Home to the White House, Life of Abraham Lincoln: Boyhood, Youth, Manhood, Assassination, Death* by William Thayer and George Bancroft, 1887/Public Domain; **146** © iStock.com/kontur-vid; **175** Eduard Kyslynskyy/Shutterstock.com; **176** Sari ONeal/Shutterstock.com; **190t** SThom/Shutterstock.com; **190b** VectorShow/Shutterstock.com; **213** Lucky-photographer/Shutterstock.com; **214** BlueOrange Studio/Shutterstock.com; **217** KieferPix/Shutterstock.com; **222** Auspicious/Shutterstock.com; **226** LuminatePhotos by judith/Shutterstock.com; **235** Holly Kuchera/Shutterstock.com; **248** nadiya_sergey/Shutterstock.com; **251** Aaron Amat/Shutterstock.com; **266** Rusla Ruseyn/Shutterstock.com; **267** © iStock.com/Trevorplatt; **268** © iStock.com/bogdanhoria; **270** Minden Pictures/SuperStock; **271** mark higgins/Shutterstock.com; **272** frederikloewer/Shutterstock.com; **273** Scanrail1/Shutterstock.com; **280** Danny Smythe/Shutterstock.com; **284** Veronika Surovtseva/Shutterstock.com; **285** ericlefrancais/Shutterstock.com; **286** Terbrana/Shutterstock.com; **6, 173, 224** © Map Resources

Acknowledgment
MY PRAIRIE YEAR by Brett Harvey, Illustrated by Deborah Kogan Ray. Text copyright © by Brett Harvey. Illustrations copyright © by Deborah Kogan Ray. Used by permission. (p. 221)

Reading 4: Voyages, Third Edition, was originally published as *Reading 4: I Met You in a Story*, Second Edition.

Greenville, South Carolina 29609

Printed in the United States of America

ISBN: 978-1-62856-076-3

15 14 13 12 11 10 9 8 7 6

Rhyme and Repetition

Rhyming words end in the same vowel and consonant sounds.
Repetition is the use of words or phrases more than once.

Mark the word that rhymes with the underlined word.

1. The daisies stood up tall under the bright <u>sun</u>.
   ○ noon ○ run ○ jump
2. The wind whistled through the <u>pines</u>.
   ○ vines ○ bike ○ cry
3. The oak tree swayed in the <u>breeze</u>.
   ○ leaf ○ froze ○ trees
4. The cheerful voices of birds filled the <u>air</u>.
   ○ warm ○ pear ○ fear
5. It was going to be a beautiful <u>day</u>.
   ○ fly ○ weigh ○ die

Underline the lines in the following poem that include repetition.

Galloping, galloping,
Journeying far.
Galloping, galloping
Under the stars.
Up the hill, up the hill,
Crunching through snow.
Down the hill, down the hill,
Homeward I go.

Creative Comparisons

A metaphor makes a comparison between two things.
A metaphor helps us see things in a new way.

Write the two things being compared in each metaphor.

1. The lake was a shining mirror for the sky.

   ________________ ________________

2. The old house is a soldier guarding the border of the town.

   ________________ ________________

3. My dog is a spinning top when he is happy.

   ________________ ________________

Choose one metaphor given above. Write how the two things are alike.

4. ____

Write the answer.

Proverbs 13:12
Hope deferred maketh the heart sick:
but when the desire cometh, it is a tree of life.

5. In his poem "Dreams," Langston Hughes uses metaphors to show that giving up on a dream makes us sad. Read Proverbs 13:12. How do our hearts feel when we do not get something we have hoped for? ____________________
6. Underline the part of the verse that uses a metaphor.
7. What is one desire or dream that God might want you to have? ____________________

Finding the Theme

The theme of a story is the author's message. Often the theme is not stated in the story. To find the theme, think about how the story ends. Ask yourself what the author wanted you to learn.

Place an *X* in the box that best states the theme of *Fire on the Mountain*.

☐ Spending the night on a mountain can be dangerous.

 People receive justice for their actions in the end.

☐ Cheating can help a person become rich and famous.

Theme: Right or Wrong?

Read the verses and answer the questions about justice.

1. Read Psalm 82:3 and Micah 6:8. How would God have wanted the rich man to treat Alemayu? ______________________

   ____

2. Read Galatians 6:7. What does this verse teach about how you treat others? ______________________

   ____

3. Did the rich man get what he deserved in the story? ______________________

   ____

4. For a short time, it appeared that Alemayu was not going to receive the reward he had earned. Did he receive justice in the end? ______________________

5. Read Matthew 16:27 and Revelation 20:12. Who will make sure that people receive justice in the end? ______________________

6. How does the Bible's teaching compare with the author's message in *Fire on the Mountain*?

   ____

   ____

   ____

Find the theme of the song.

On the cross, Jesus took the punishment that people deserve for their sins. Romans 6:23 says that a person who places his trust in Jesus receives the undeserved gift of eternal life. The poet Fanny Crosby wrote a song to thank Jesus for what He did for her on the cross. Underline the line that tells the theme of her song.

I think of my blessed Redeemer,
I think of Him all the day long;
I sing, for I cannot be silent;
His love is the theme of my song.

Chanticleer and Nebuchadnezzar

Answer the following questions.

1. What is the difference between a fable and a Bible account? ______

2. What character trait do Chanticleer and Nebuchadnezzar have in common? ______
3. What do the themes of both selections say about pride? ______

4. What character trait is the opposite of pride? ______
5. How does Chanticleer change? What causes the change? ______

6. How did Nebuchadnezzar change? What caused the change? ______

Pride and Humility

The Bible says much about pride and humility. The verses below tell how God views these two character traits.

Proverbs 8:13

The fear of the Lord is to hate evil: pride, and arrogancy, and the evil way, and the froward mouth, do I hate.

Proverbs 22:4

By humility and the fear of the Lord are riches, and honour, and life.

James 4:6*b*

God resisteth the proud, but giveth grace unto the humble.

James 4:10

Humble yourselves in the sight of the Lord, and he shall lift you up.

1 Peter 5:5*b*

Be clothed with humility: for God resisteth the proud, and giveth grace to the humble.

Read the verses above and answer the questions.

1. How does God feel about pride and those who are proud? ______________________

____

2. How can pride keep you from obeying God? ______________________

____

____

3. How does God feel about humility and those who are humble? ______________________

____

____

4. How do people show humility when they accept salvation? ______________________

____

What Does G[illegible]d Say?

A concordance is [illegible]ool to study the Bible. Keywords are listed alphabetically, b[illegible] the references are in Bible order. Most concordances show the keywo[illegible] only as an initial in the phrases. Concordances abbreviate, or sh[illegible]ten, Bible book names. For the concordance selection below, Proverbs [illegible]as been abbreviated "Prov." If you have an electronic device, search t[illegible] keyword using an online concordance.

anger		angry	
Prov. 15[illegible]	grievous words stir up *a*	Prov. 14:17	He that is soon *a*
1[illegible]18	he that is slow to *a*	22:24	Make no friendship with an *a* man
[illegible]:11	The discretion of a man deferreth his *a*	29:22	An *a* man stirreth up strife

Us[illegible]e c[illegible]ordance entries above and your Bible to complete the chart bel[illegible] C[illegible]se three verses. Write the references and tell in your own words wha[illegible] [illegible]arned about anger or being angry.

[illegible]Verse reference	What does God's Word tell me about anger?

What Temper?

Read each question. Write your answer.

1. What did Ben learn about a person's temper from reading *Psychology Today*? ______________

2. What did Ben learn about a person's temper when he read Proverbs 16:32? ______________

3. Can you think of a time when you were angry? Briefly describe the situation. ______________

4. What would be the best way for you to handle a similar situation in the future? ______________

5. Choose one of the verses used in the Bible study on anger. Write the reference and verse in the box below and work on memorizing the verse.

Brain Power

Read each question. Write your answer.

1. Is informational text fiction or nonfiction? ______________________________

2. What is the main idea of the article? ______________________________

____

Read each statement. Mark the details that support the main idea of the article.

○ The human brain is faster than a computer.

○ The human brain was designed by God to change.

○ A blind person often loses his other senses, like hearing, from lack of use.

○ Humans become better at a skill with practice because of the brain's flexibility.

○ A person with a brain injury can never recover.

○ With practice, a person will become better at sports or a subject in school.

Read each description. Place an *X* beside anything that is *not* an example of informational text.

______ a newspaper article about the town zoo

______ a story about a boy's trip to Mars

______ a magazine article about mountain climbing

______ a history textbook

______ a comic book about a talking giraffe

Brainy Terms

In the spaces below, write the words from the word bank that are described by the following definitions. The circled letters spell out a word. Once you have figured out what the word is, fill in the blanks to complete the statement at the bottom.

adapt	flexible	heightened
fascinating	hardwired	perform

1. ___ ___ ___ ___ ___ ___ ___ ___
2. ___ ___ ___ ___ ___ ___ ___
3. ___ ___ ___ ___ ___
4. ___ ___ ___ ___ ___ ___ ___ ___ ___
5. ___ ___ ___ ___ ___ ___ ___ ___ ___ ___
6. ___ ___ ___ ___ ___ ___ ___ ___ ___ ___ ___

1. having ability to change
2. to work or function
3. to change or get used to
4. not changeable; having permanent connections
5. increased; raised or sharpened
6. very or extremely interesting

God created our ___ ___ ___ ___ ___ ___ to be flexible.

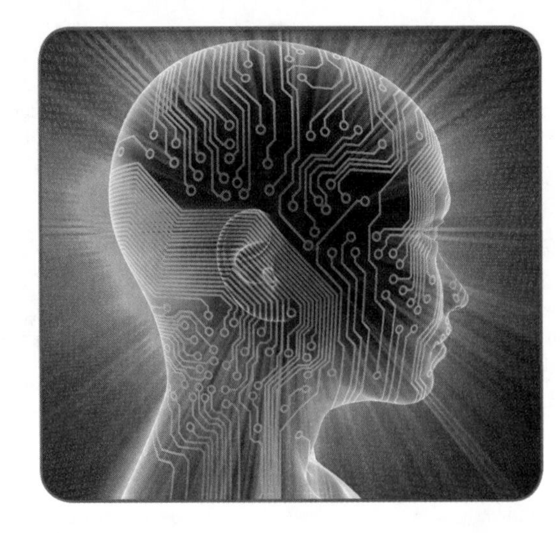

Follow the procedure on page 70 of the Student Text. On the line under the ruler, write down the point where your fingers caught the ruler. Draw a line on the ruler to mark the point. Lightly shade the ruler from the bottom of the ruler up to your line. Repeat the entire procedure four more times.

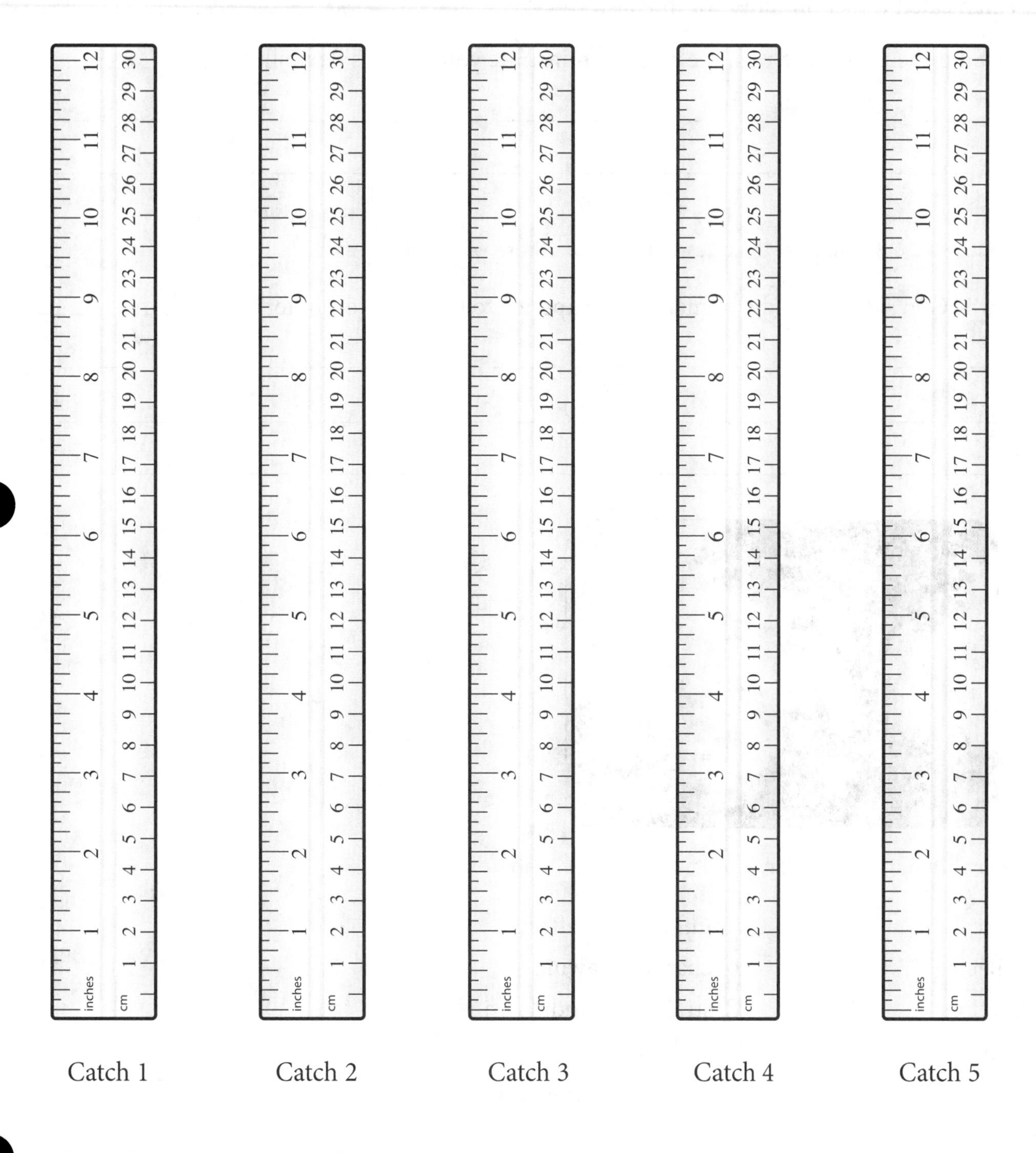

Your Flexible Brain

Study the shaded rulers and the recorded results of each procedure. Answer the questions.

1. Which catch (reaction time) was the slowest? ______________________
2. Which catch (reaction time) was the fastest? ______________________
3. How did the procedure with the ruler demonstrate your brain's flexibility? ______________________

____

____

Read Genesis 1:26–27. Answer the question based on these verses and the article.

4. How is God's design of the human brain superior to that of a computer? ______________________

____

____

____

Draw a line from the vocabulary word to the correct definition.

5. vertical	A. influence or effect
6. impact	B. chart or drawing
7. reaction	C. straight up and down
8. graph	D. grab quickly
9. snatch	E. action in response to something

Haiku

____

Write an *H* beside each statement that correctly describes a haiku.

_______ The haiku poem came from Japan.

_______ All haiku poems use rhyming words.

_______ Each line of a haiku poem has a certain number of syllables.

_______ Haiku poems have three lines.

_______ Haiku poems are considered to be autobiographies.

_______ Traditional haiku poems describe some part of nature.

Read the haiku. Write the number of syllables in each line.
Draw a picture showing what the haiku describes.

A floating green log—	Line 1: _______ syllables
Golden eyes search the water.	Line 2: _______ syllables
Sharp teeth snap for fish.	Line 3: _______ syllables

My Haiku

Writing a haiku requires a lot of thought. A poet must choose the subject of the haiku. The poet then thinks about how to describe the subject within the 5-7-5 syllabic pattern. Carefully chosen words create a picture that appeals to the reader's senses.

Follow the steps for writing your own haiku. Write your ideas in the second column.

Subject of my haiku What part of nature is beautiful or interesting to me?	____ ____ ____ ____
Words What words describe the subject? How does it look, sound, smell, feel, or taste? What do I want the reader to feel or see while reading my haiku?	____ ____ ____ ____

Use the ideas you wrote in the box above to create your own haiku. Follow the 5-7-5 syllabic pattern.

______

______

______

Continue the Story

Brainstorm with a partner about how you would continue the folktale after Kenjii and his wife become rich. Choose two or three questions from below. Use your answers to create your own ending. Read your ending to your partner.

Kenjii and his wife	Brainstorm
What do they do with their gold?	
Do they help others with their money, or do they spend it on themselves?	
Do they have enough gold to last the rest of their lives, or do they run out?	
Does Kenjii become deceitful and selfish like Ichiro?	
How will they respond if someone steals their gold?	
If Kenjii or his wife becomes sick, will their riches heal them?	
If Kenjii's wife dies, will his riches comfort him?	

Evaluate My Story

Proverbs 11:28

He that trusteth in his riches shall fall:
but the righteous shall flourish as a branch.

Proverbs 13:7

There is that maketh himself rich,
yet hath nothing:
there is that maketh himself poor,
yet hath great riches.

Proverbs 28:6

Better is the poor that walketh in his uprightness,
than he that is perverse in his ways,
though he be rich.

2 Thessalonians 3:10

For even when we were with you,
this we commanded you,
that if any would not work,
neither should he eat.

Read the Bible verses. Answer the questions about your ending to the folktale. Write the references of any verses that may apply.

1. Does Kenjii continue to trust in his wealth for happiness? ______________________

____

2. Does Kenjii learn any valuable lessons? ______________________

____

____

3. Which of the above verses fit the ending you created? ______________________

____

____

Free Verse

Mark each statement *T* for true or *F* for false.

______ 1. Free verse is a kind of poetry.

______ 2. Free verse does not have a regular pattern of rhyme.

______ 3. A free verse poem does not create any pictures in our minds.

______ 4. Free verse has a regular pattern of rhythm.

______ 5. A free verse poem expresses ideas or feelings.

Read each poem and answer the questions.

Daisies

Daisies are girls
spinning in white dresses,
singing for joy,
and waving bright yellow
handkerchiefs
at the sky.

____

One Bird

One last bird in autumn
waits silent as snow
on the bare limb of a birch tree.
It leans into the wind,
fluffing its feathers
for a solo flight.

____

happy	angry	lonely

6. Choose the word from the word bank that best describes the mood of each poem. Write it in the blank below the poem.
7. "Daisies" includes a metaphor. What two things are being compared?

   ____

8. Underline the line in "One Bird" that contains a simile.

Metaphor and Simile

If the comparison is a metaphor, write an *M* in the blank. If the comparison is a simile, write an *S* in the blank, and underline *like* or *as*.

_______ 1. The warm, slow sun came up like bread rising in a pan.

_______ 2. Two birds were black drops of ink on a page of sky.

_______ 3. Clouds floated like purple islands in a rosy lake.

_______ 4. The wind was as soft as a baby's blanket brushing my skin.

_______ 5. The car horn was a trumpet blast in the quiet morning.

_______ 6. The garden was a sea of bright color beside the gray fence.

Create a simile or a metaphor to complete each comparison.

7. Our cat is as _______________ as _______________________________

8. Ice cream is as _______________ as _______________________________

9. The sun feels like ____

____

10. A winter day is ____

____

Gifted Hands

Put the events of Ben's life in the correct order. Use numbers 1–5.

_______ God gave Ben victory over his bad temper.

_______ Ben discovered that reading books would help him in all his subjects at school.

_______ A doctor discovered that Ben needed glasses.

_______ Ben tried to kill his friend.

_______ Ben's classmates nicknamed him "Dummy."

Choose two vocabulary words from the box. Write a sentence showing the correct meaning for each one. Use the Glossary as needed.

analyze	insight	invaluable	judgmental	neurosurgery	philosophy

1. _______________

2. _______________

Read each question. Write your answer.

3. How well did Sonya's method work for helping to improve Ben's grades? _______________

4. How well did Ben's method work for solving the problem with his bad temper? _______________

5. Think about a problem you may be having in your life. Use a separate sheet of paper to write out a prayer. Is there something you should confess to God? Is there something you should ask God to do for you?

Mark the answer.

6. Because of the special abilities God gave to Ben Carson, he became very good at ___.
   - ○ basketball
   - ○ neurosurgery
7. According to Ben's acrostic, being nice means you ___.
   - ○ help someone who is struggling
   - ○ talk about a person behind his back
8. Ben believes that America will be a better nation if ___.
   - ○ its citizens live by God's truths
   - ○ its citizens do not talk about God in public

Write the answer.

9. How would you rearrange the words in Dr. Carson's acrostic from most important to least important?

Read the paragraphs below. Choose one paragraph and write how you would solve the problem.

10a. You are on the playground at recess. You have just made friends with a new student. Your two best friends join you and your new friend. They make fun of the new student. What will you do?

10b. You go to the store with a friend. You see your friend take something off the shelf. He puts the item in his pocket without paying for it. What will you do?

Create a Character

Choose an animal to write about. Draw a picture of the animal, and give it a name.

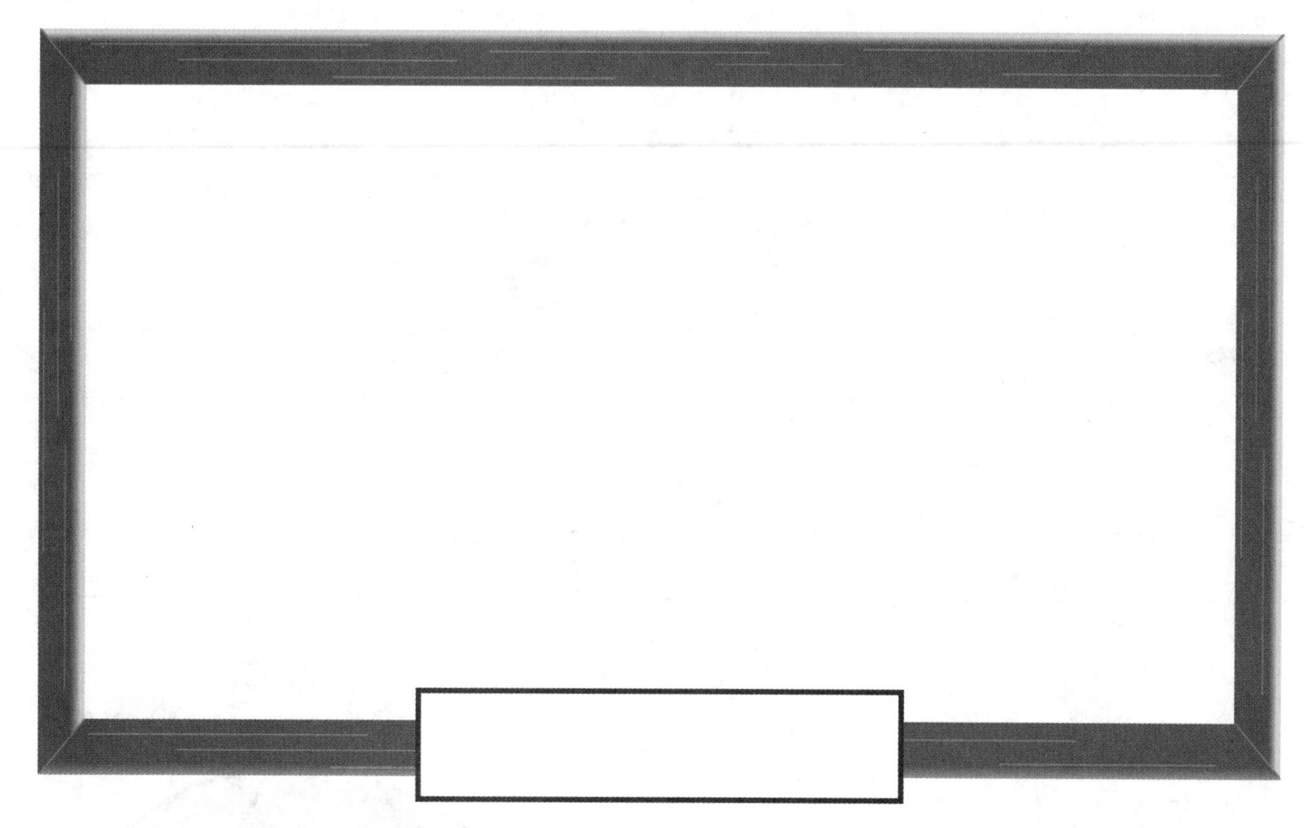

Create a character web for your animal. Place its name in the center oval. Add traits and details in the surrounding ovals.

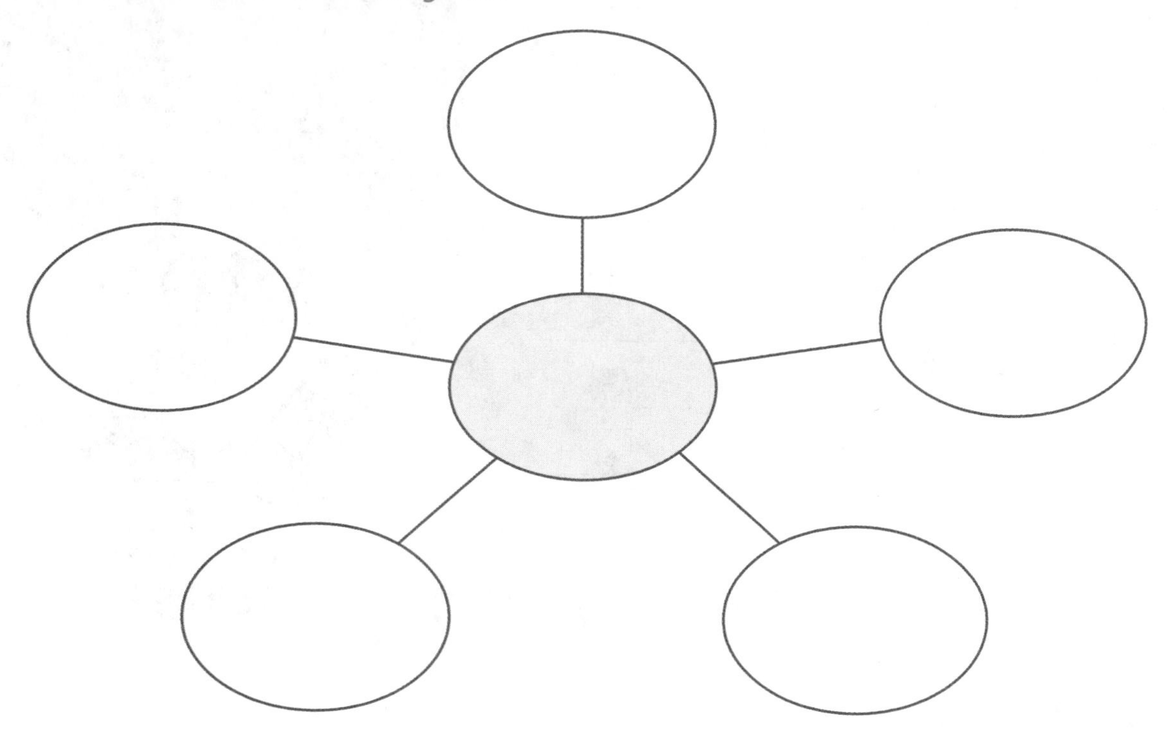

Fun with Fantasy

Write a paragraph about the animal character you created. Be sure to include something that could not happen in real life.

Limericks

Use two different colors to circle the sets of rhyming words found at the end of the lines of the limerick.

There once was a normal-sized cat;
She ate, and she ate, and got fat;
Her stomach grew round
And dragged on the ground;
But she kept the floor swept—that was that!

Write the color of the circles in the order they appear in the poem. Note the pattern.

__________, __________, __________, __________, __________

Mark the correct answer.

1. What rhyming pattern does a limerick follow?
   ○ ababa ○ abaab ○ aabba
2. Limericks usually ___.
   ○ entertain ○ inform ○ teach
3. A limerick has ___.
   ○ two short lines and two long lines
   ○ two short lines and three long lines
   ○ three short lines and two long lines

Write the letter of the picture that shows the meaning of each word.

_____ 4. bonnet

_____ 5. critter

_____ 6. hullabaloo

A.

B.

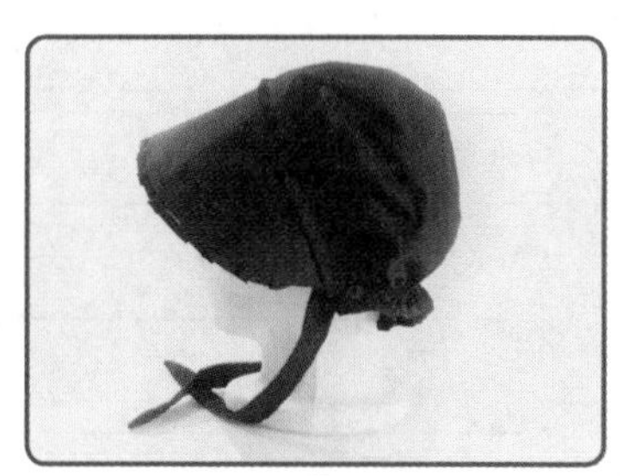
C.

Write a Limerick

Write the rhyming words to complete the limerick.

afar	car	star

I opened the door to my ______________,

Out toppled a bright shining ______________;

It gleamed and it shone

Right through to my bones;

Then it flew off and twinkled ______________.

Write your own limerick.

To get started, choose a one-syllable noun that represents an interesting topic. Next, write several other words that rhyme with the word you chose. Finally, work to match the rhythm and rhyme pattern of a limerick. Remember to add some humor.

Topic

____

Rhyming words

______________ ______________

______________ ______________

____

____

____

____

____

Illustrate your limerick on a separate sheet of paper.

A Fable or a Parable

____

List the three main characters in the "Parable of the Prodigal Son." Tell something you learned from each one.

1. ______________________________

____

2. ______________________________

____

3. ______________________________

____

Write each phrase on the appropriate side of the T-chart.

A.	B.	C.
animals that talk	spiritual lesson	Bible supports teaching
realistic characters	moral	Bible may or may not support teaching

Fable	Parable
A. ______________	A. ______________
B. ______________	B. ______________
C. ______________	C. ______________
______________	______________

Evaluate a Moral

Read the fable. Mark each answer.

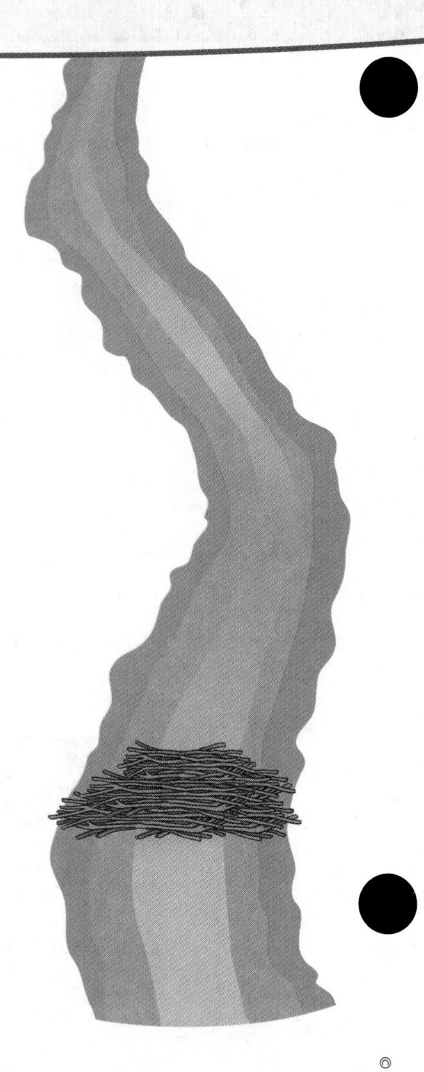

A widow beaver lived in a sturdy home on the river with her five grown sons. Each son had a special gift. One was good at finding the perfect sticks to keep the dam strong. One was skilled at digging the mud to hold the dam together. Another knew how to use sticks and mud to repair the dam. The strongest son was good at lifting the sticks into place. And the youngest could predict the weather and warn his family of possible flooding.

Mother beaver was growing weaker every day. She loved her sons, but they quarreled daily about who had the greatest ability. She wanted them to work together to continue to have a strong dam.

One day she instructed each son to gather two sticks from the riverbank. She had each beaver break one of his sticks in half. Each beaver broke the single stick with ease. Next, she had her sons place their other stick in a pile. She asked one of the brothers to stack and tie the sticks into a bundle. Finally, she directed each of her sons to try to break the bundle of sticks. One by one they failed. Even the strongest son was unable to snap the bundle in half.

The mother beaver gently explained that each beaver was weak when he stood alone. Together they could be strong.

1. What is the moral of this fable?
   - ○ A successful dam needs lots of beavers.
   - ○ We are stronger when we work together.
   - ○ Quarreling makes things better.

2. Which of these verses supports the truth of this moral?
   - ○ "Two are better than one; because they have a good reward for their labour." (Ecclesiastes 4:9)
   - ○ "Ask, and it shall be given you." (Matthew 7:7*a*)
   - ○ "Forgiving one another . . . even as Christ forgave you." (Colossians 3:13)

3. Can you trust the lesson of this fable?
   - ○ No, you cannot trust a man's words.
   - ○ Yes, smart men teach this same idea.
   - ○ Yes, the Bible teaches this same truth.

4. Where does wisdom comes from?
   - ○ a person who has gone to school for many years
   - ○ a mighty king or president
   - ○ the one true God and His Word

My Brother's Keeper

The moral of the tale "Two Brothers" is that we should put the needs of others before our own needs.

Mark the correct answer that completes each sentence.

1. The married brother thinks the equal division of the land is not fair because his unmarried brother ___.
   - ○ has no children to feed
   - ○ has no one who will care for him in his old age
   - ○ is lazy and is not using the land well

2. The irony in this folktale is that ___.
   - ○ both brothers have the same idea, but neither one knows what the other is thinking and doing
   - ○ both brothers end up losing their land to a rich man
   - ○ both brothers are being selfish by stealing grain at night from one another

Read the verses. On the line provided, explain the meaning of each verse.

3. "Look not every man on his own things, but every man also on the things of others" (Philippians 2:4). ______________________________

   ____

4. "Let no man seek his own, but every man another's wealth" (1 Corinthians 10:24).

   ____

   ____

Read the directions. On your own paper, write your answers.

5. Think back over the last week. Identify one situation in which you could have put another person's needs above your own and you did not.
6. Think back over the last week. Identify one situation in which you could have put another person's needs above your own and you did.

What You Know About Words

Read the sentences in your Student Text that contain each vocabulary word. Match each word with its definition.

_______ 1. bemused (page 117)

_______ 2. dignity (page 116)

_______ 3. haul (page 118)

_______ 4. inherit (page 115)

_______ 5. silo (page 116)

A. load

B. to be puzzled or confused

C. underground pit dug for storing grain

D. to receive something from someone who has died

E. condition of being worthy of respect or honor

Choose three words from the list above. Write each word on a bundle of wheat below. Then write an interesting sentence using each word.

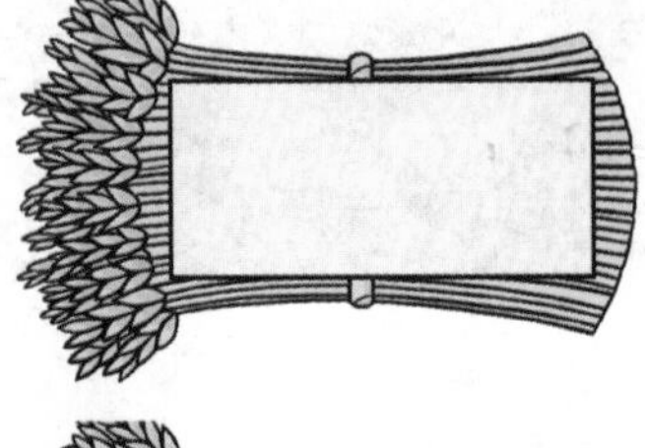

6. ____

____

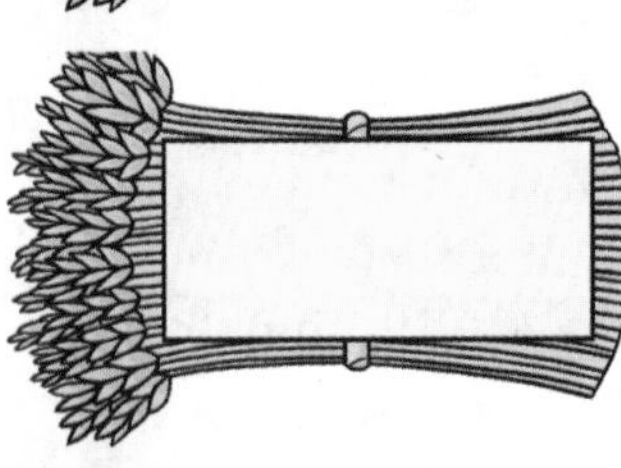

7. ____

____

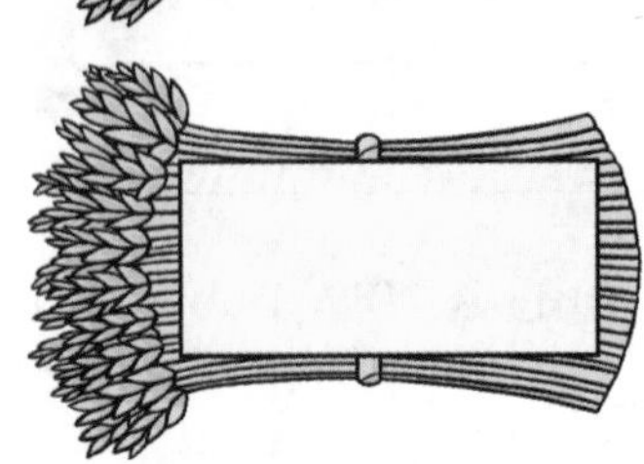

8. ____

____

God's Love

Look up Ephesians 2:4–9. Use the words from the word bank to complete what the verses teach.

dead	faith	freely given	gift
grace	love	mercy	

Ephesians 2:4

God is rich in ________________. He sent Jesus to die for us.

Ephesians 2:5

We are all ________________ in sin.

Ephesians 2:8–9

We are saved by ________________ through ________________. None of us can earn God's ________________.

He does not love us because we have earned His love. God's love is ________________.

Our salvation is a ________________ from God.

Read Mamá's explanation to Ana about the best kind of love on page 142. Answer the questions.

1. What does Mamá say about the best kind of love? ________________

____

2. How does Mamá's idea of love compare to God's love? ________________

____

Loving Others

God loves us because He is merciful and kind. God offers salvation to all people because His love is unconditional. God even provides food and shelter for people who hate Him because His love is unconditional. There is nothing we can do or not do to earn this love. Because God loves us, we must love others. Loving others may require sacrifice. It may be hard to love people who are not nice. God will help us to show the right kind of love—His unconditional love—to others.

Choose a person you know. Complete this page to help you identify ways you can show God's unconditional love to that person.

Person (Writing a name is optional, but think of a specific person.) ______________________

____

I can show love to this person by ______________________

____

____

I can show love to this person even when I am not around this person by ______________________

____

____

I may have to sacrifice to show love to this person by ______________________

____

____

Write a prayer for this person. ______________________

____

____

____

____

The Bridge

An author uses a symbol to give a story deeper meaning. A symbol may have different meanings at different times in the story. The story "Janwahr's Bridge" has a symbol with several meanings.

Mark the correct answer.

1. What person or thing does the title, "Janwahr's Bridge," refer to in the story?
   - ○ the river
   - ○ Danzee, the dragon
   - ○ King Rolday
   - ○ Janwahr

Think about how Danzee is important to the meaning of the title and story. Mark each statement that shows what Danzee represents at different times in the story.

2. At the beginning of the story, Danzee is ___.
   - ○ a baby dragon without a mother
   - ○ a friend who creates a bridge between Janwahr's blindness and his feeling like other boys
3. In the middle of the story, Danzee is ___.
   - ○ a guardian of the river against other water creatures
   - ○ a real bridge that helps the princess cross the river to safety
4. At the end of the story, Danzee is ___.
   - ○ a friend who creates a bridge between Janwahr's lack of confidence and his feeling like a true prince
   - ○ a fierce dragon that breathes fire on the enemy army

Friendship

We can have many types of friends. Brothers, sisters, and cousins can be our friends. Sometimes, we have friends from school or church. Our friends can also be any age, such as an elderly neighbor. Even a pet can be a friend. In "Janwahr's Bridge," Janwahr valued his friendship with a dragon named Danzee.

Think about one of your friends. Draw a picture of this friend in the middle oval. Describe your friendship in the ovals around the picture.

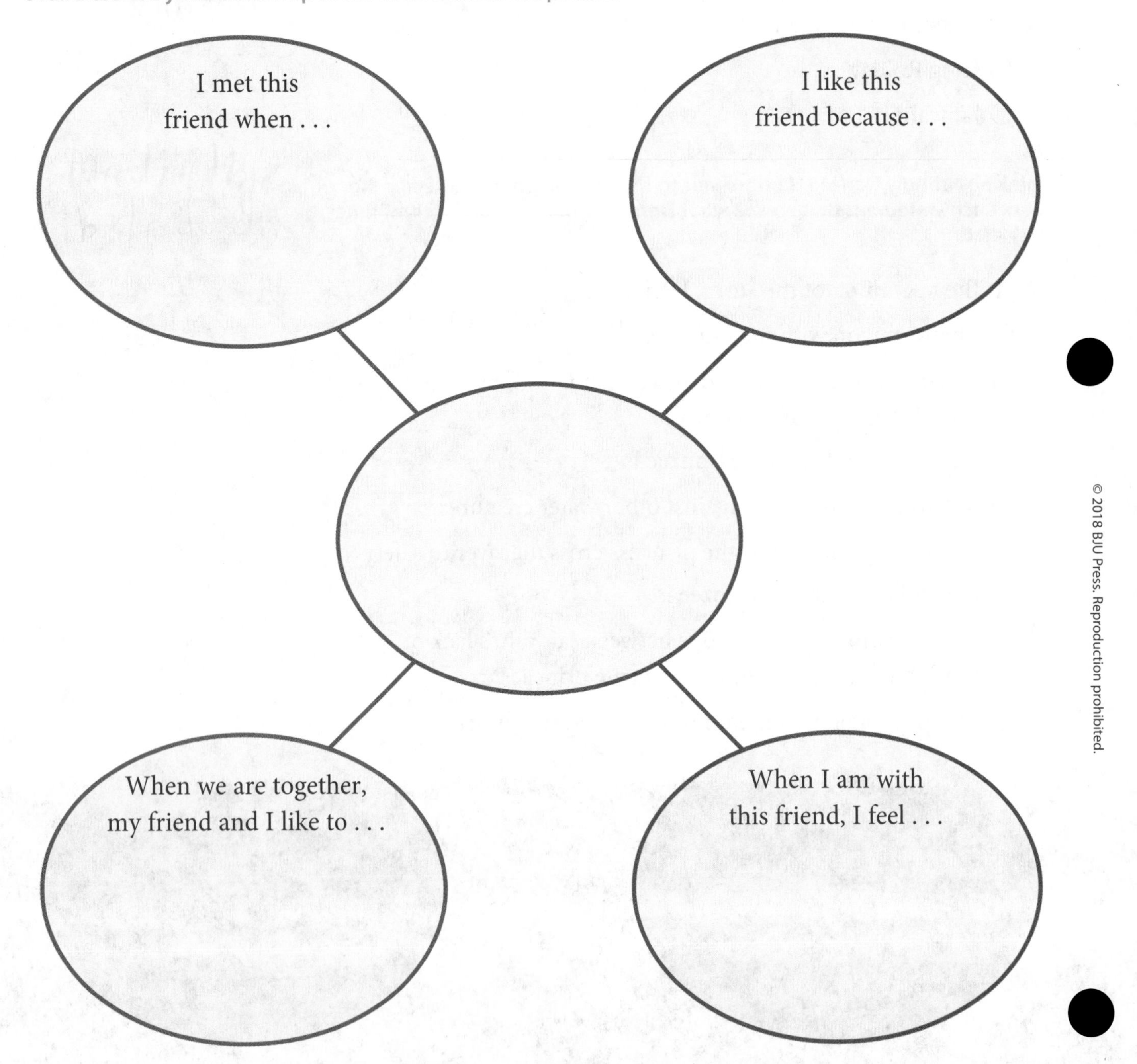

Cause and Effect

Mark five emotions Elizabeth Ann displays.

○ relief ○ pride ○ terror ○ fright ○ calmness

○ guilt ○ cheerfulness ○ nervousness ○ boredom ○ anger

An effect is something that happens. A cause is why something happens. Sometimes there is more than one cause for what happens in a story, and sometimes there is more than one effect from a cause.

Mark one or more causes for each effect.

1. **Effect:** Elizabeth Ann's knees are knocking, and she must be carried off the train.
   Cause(s):
   ○ She is thinking of the strange faces she is going to meet.
   ○ She is sick from the lunch she ate.
   ○ She is planning to run away, and the conductor has to stop her.

2. **Effect:** Uncle Henry hands Elizabeth Ann the reins.
   Cause(s):
   ○ Uncle Henry is tired from the trip to town, and he wants to take a nap.
   ○ Uncle Henry is aware that Elizabeth Ann is frightened and wants to distract her.
   ○ Uncle Henry wants to work on some figures.

Mark one or more effects for each cause.

3. **Cause:** Because Aunt Frances has always helped Elizabeth Ann "over the hard places," ____.
   Effect(s):
   ○ Elizabeth Ann has never discovered anything on her own
   ○ Elizabeth Ann is excited to visit new places and meet new people
   ○ Elizabeth Ann cannot think quickly enough to tell her right hand from her left hand

4. **Cause:** Because Elizabeth Ann successfully drives the wagon, ____.
   Effect(s):
   ○ she is proud of her accomplishment
   ○ she forgets how afraid she is of Uncle Henry and speaks to him
   ○ she realizes she does not need to know her right hand from her left hand

On Track with Synonyms

Looking at how a word is used in a sentence can help you decide the meaning of that word.

Read each sentence. Choose a synonym for the colored word from the choices provided. Write the letter in the blank.

_______ 1. The **dreadful** flood washed away the farmer's crops.

_______ 2. It is important to **assert** the truth of the Bible.

_______ 3. Tony thought that the orange-and-red car looked **hideous**.

_______ 4. "It is **essential** that all players attend the meeting," said the coach.

_______ 5. "Let me **reassure** you," said Lois. "The flower arrangement will look beautiful on the table."

_______ 6. Larry was very **apprehensive** about riding the giant roller coaster.

A. declare

B. necessary

C. nervous

D. ugly

E. encourage

F. awful

What Happened and Why?

Read the sentences below the chart. Write each sentence in the correct box to complete the chart.

Cause (Why?)	Effect (What happened?)
Elizabeth Ann is told where to hang her cape and coat.	
	• Elizabeth Ann feels millions of miles away from Aunt Frances. • She believes there is nobody to take care of her. • Her throat feels tight. • Her eyes begin to water.
	• Elizabeth Ann cannot speak. • She is distracted from feeling homesick.
No one makes Elizabeth Ann eat baked beans during dinner.	

- Elizabeth Ann is given a kitten.
- Elizabeth Ann feels sorry for herself, and for the first time ever, she must take care of her own wraps.
- Elizabeth Ann is relieved.
- No one asks Elizabeth Ann how she "stood the trip."

Read each question. Write your answer.

1. What reason might Aunt Abigail and Cousin Ann have for calling Elizabeth Ann "Betsy"?

____

____

2. How do we know that Aunt Abigail may have noticed Elizabeth Ann's "miserable, homesick eyes"? ______________________________

Which Word?

Read the sentences. Write the word that completes each sentence.

detest	gravely	resolution
evidently	pester	speculative

1. Sandy looked ______________________ at the sick dog and said, "He's going to need to see the vet."
2. "I ______________________ running in the cold rain," said Henry.
3. ______________________, the girl broke the window when she threw the ball.
4. Greg's little brother would ______________________ him again and again for candy.
5. Feeling ______________________, Tom took a second look at the ad for the new bike.
6. "My ______________________ is to clean my room once a week," said Juan.

Use your Student Text to find the vocabulary words that are synonyms of the underlined words below. Mark the correct answer for each question.

7. Who hates baked beans? (page 194)

   ○ Elizabeth Ann ○ Aunt Frances ○ Cousin Ann

8. Who bothers Aunt Abigail? (page 196)

   ○ Uncle Henry ○ Elizabeth Ann ○ the kitten

9. Who watches Elizabeth Ann with uncertain eyes? (page 196)

   ○ the horses ○ the kitten ○ Uncle Henry

10. Who has determined not to refer to Aunt Abigail as "aunt"? (page 197)

   ○ Cousin Ann ○ Elizabeth Ann ○ Aunt Frances

Betsy Holds the Reins

____

Mark the answer that completes each sentence.

1. When Uncle Henry first hands Elizabeth Ann the reins, she feels ___.
   ○ frightened ○ proud ○ angry

2. When Elizabeth Ann makes the right decisions while driving the wagon, she feels ___.
   ○ frightened ○ proud ○ angry

3. When Elizabeth Ann first arrives in the Putney kitchen, she feels ___.
   ○ loved ○ relieved ○ sorry for herself

4. When the Putneys let Elizabeth Ann decide for herself what she is going to eat for supper, she feels ___.
   ○ loved ○ relieved ○ sorry for herself

5. When Elizabeth Ann is getting ready for bed, she feels ___.
   ○ miserable ○ excited ○ wanted

6. When Aunt Abigail tells Elizabeth Ann that it is "going to be real nice having a little girl in the house again," Elizabeth Ann feels ___.
   ○ miserable ○ excited ○ wanted

Read each statement and identify the character described.
Write the correct letter in the blank.

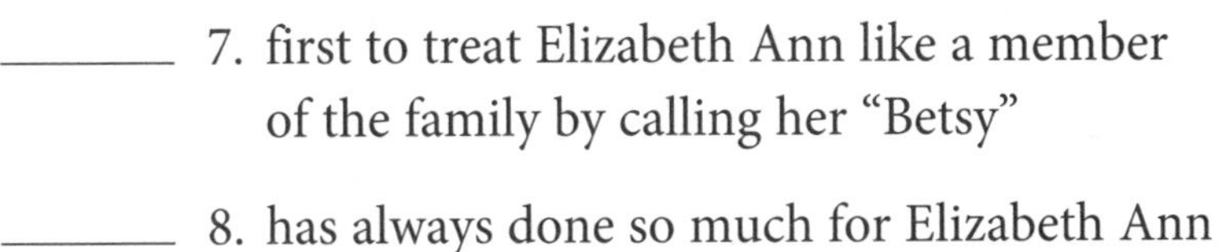

A. Uncle Henry B. Aunt Abigail C. Cousin Ann D. Aunt Frances

_______ 7. first to treat Elizabeth Ann like a member of the family by calling her "Betsy"

_______ 8. has always done so much for Elizabeth Ann that she does not think for herself

_______ 9. distracts Elizabeth Ann from feeling homesick by giving her a kitten

_______ 10. helps Elizabeth Ann gain confidence by letting her decide how to get the wagon out of a ditch

Betsy Holds the Reins

Match each word with the correct definition.

_______ 11. crook (page 202)

_______ 12. grotesque (page 206)

_______ 13. miserable (page 202)

_______ 14. nightcap (page 201)

_______ 15. pervasive (page 203)

_______ 16. assert (page 181)

_______ 17. gravely (page 194)

_______ 18. dreadful (page 181)

A. terrible

B. spread throughout

C. a cloth hat worn in bed

D. to bend or curve

E. very unhappy

F. seriously

G. odd or distorted

H. to strongly declare

Read the verse and the following statements. Write your answer.

Proverbs 27:17

Iron sharpeneth iron;
so a man sharpeneth the
countenance of his friend.

"Iron sharpeneth iron" is a metaphor to teach that one person's words or actions can help another person to change and improve.

In this verse, "countenance" refers to the whole person. To "sharpen the countenance" means to encourage or help someone to grow inwardly.

19. Choose either Uncle Henry or Aunt Abigail. Explain how his or her words and actions support the teachings of Proverbs 27:17.

____

____

____

____

____

Growing Up

Sometimes a story title is a symbol. This means that it has more than one meaning. The literal meaning of the title describes what actually happens in the story. But the title may also have a symbolic meaning that helps us to understand an important idea in the story.

Complete the chart.

Title	Literal meaning	Symbolic meaning
"Janwahr's Bridge"		Danzee provides a bridge for blind Prince Janwahr to grow as a leader and to gain confidence as a member of the royal family.
"Betsy Holds the Reins"	Uncle Henry hands Elizabeth Ann the reins to the horses on the way home from the railroad station.	

Mark two correct answers for each question.

1. How did Aunt Frances prevent Elizabeth Ann from being in control?
   - ○ Aunt Frances encouraged Elizabeth Ann to think for herself.
   - ○ Aunt Frances made all the hard decisions for Elizabeth Ann.
   - ○ Aunt Frances's constant presence and care kept Elizabeth Ann from learning and growing.
2. When is Elizabeth Ann in control?
   - ○ when she gets the wagon out of the ditch
   - ○ when she keeps the horses in the middle of the road
   - ○ when the conductor carries her off the train
3. How does being in control change Elizabeth Ann?
   - ○ She is more confident.
   - ○ She is overtaken with a dreadful terror.
   - ○ She is able to think for herself and make important decisions more quickly.

Root Words

bicycle	grave	perfume	telegraph
centimeter	gravity	permit	thermometer
graphic	inspect	spectacles	tricycle

Read the chart. Using each root word, write two examples of English words from the word bank. The first one has been done for you.

Latin or Greek root	Meaning	English words	
cycl from Greek	circle, ring	**cycl**e	bicycle, tricycle
graph from Greek	write	auto**graph**	____________ ____________
gravis from Latin	heavy, weighty	**grav**ely	____________ ____________
meter from Greek	measure	baro**meter**	____________ ____________
per from Latin	through	**per**vasive	____________ ____________
spec from Latin	look, see	**spec**ulative	____________ ____________

Memories

Write one of the dog's memories in each cloud.

Read the question. Write the answer.

How does the title "Stories" support the theme? ______

______

Burning Terms

Match each definition with the vocabulary word.

_______ 1. not gentle or careful

_______ 2. one who fights for or defends someone else

_______ 3. to play actively

_______ 4. a flame

_______ 5. to get something by being gentle or nice

_______ 6. to polish or shine

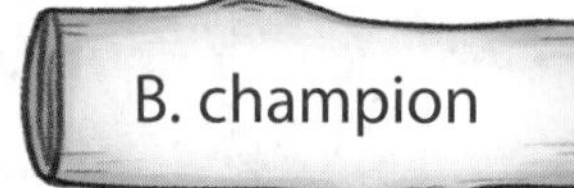

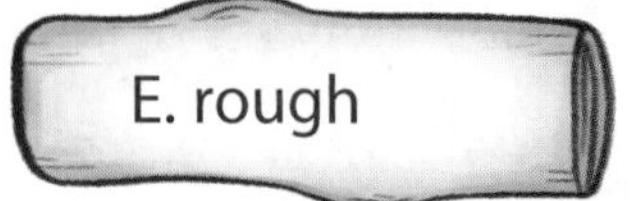

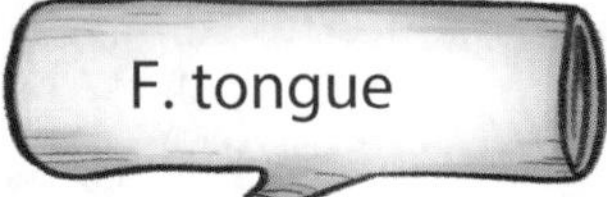

Read each sentence. Underline the example of onomatopoeia.

7. The ticktock of the grandfather clock put Sarah to sleep.
8. Josh made a huge splash when he jumped into the pond.
9. The large truck beeped as it backed up to the loading dock.
10. A wolf howled in the forest as the sun was setting.
11. Rosa covered her ears as the jet roared down the runway.

Find and circle each vocabulary word from above. Words can be found horizontally, vertically, diagonally, backward, or forward.

A	N	E	C	Z	Q	B	T	E
C	H	O	X	L	P	U	A	H
J	A	N	I	O	T	F	S	G
X	R	Z	H	P	O	F	W	U
B	I	W	M	I	M	H	L	O
U	W	O	B	J	Q	A	X	R
Z	R	O	A	Y	X	I	H	N
Q	N	K	C	T	E	M	O	C
M	T	O	N	G	U	E	X	I

Comparing Poems

Mark the correct answer. Use your Venn diagram to help you as needed.

1. A poem's theme is its ____.
   - ○ title ○ message ○ rhythm
2. Poems that look at a similar topic in different ways ____.
   - ○ can help us see differences in theme
   - ○ are usually too much alike in their message
   - ○ are always by the same author
3. Which statement is true of "Seashells" and "maggie and milly and molly and may"?
   - ○ Both poems have the same theme.
   - ○ Both poems include rhyme.
   - ○ Both poems include spelling mistakes.
4. Which statement is true only of the poem "Seashells"?
   - ○ It tells about shells.
   - ○ It includes rhyme.
   - ○ It has a special shape on the page.
5. Which statement is true only of the poem "maggie and milly and molly and may"?
   - ○ It talks about creatures who live on the beach.
   - ○ It has an important theme about people.
   - ○ Its shape lets us see what it is about.

Write a sentence that tells which poem you like better and why.

6. ______________________________

____

Shape Up!

A free verse poem does not have a regular pattern of rhythm and rhyme.

Draw the outline of a creature that lives in the ocean. Write a free verse poem about the creature inside the outline.

Write the correct vocabulary word by the leg of the sea star.

befriend	languid
retired	stranded

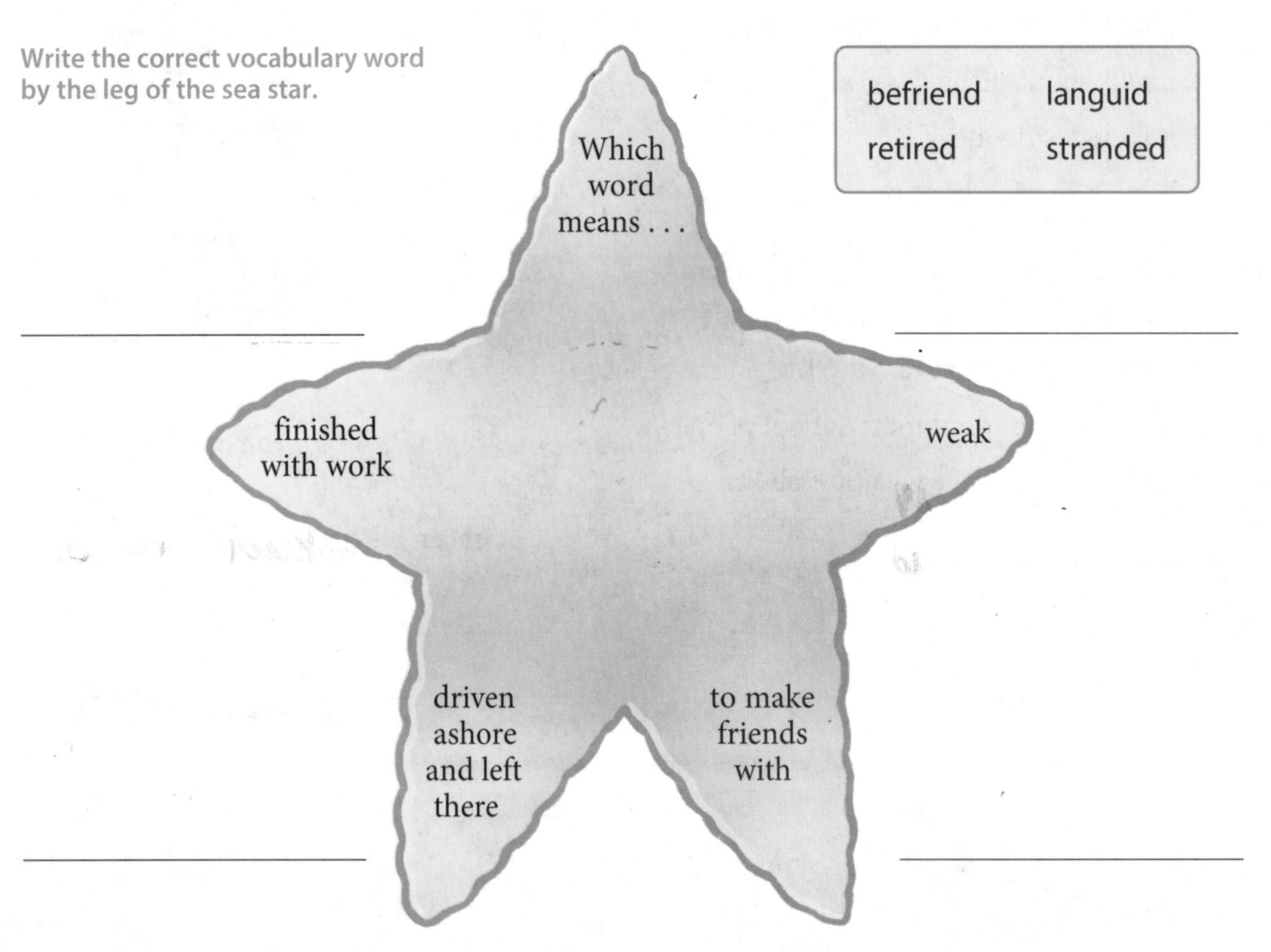

Myth or Truth?

Angelina

Work with a partner to complete the page.

Student 1: You live in ancient Greece. Your parents have taught you the Greek myth about Demeter and Persephone. You believe it is true. One day your younger brother notices that the leaves are falling from the trees and the air feels colder. He asks you why this is happening.

What would you tell him? A Godess wuse looking for here doter and forgot to tell the plants growe

Can these gods be trusted to care for your world? Why or why not? no, becuse the reele god is in Control of ower wrold

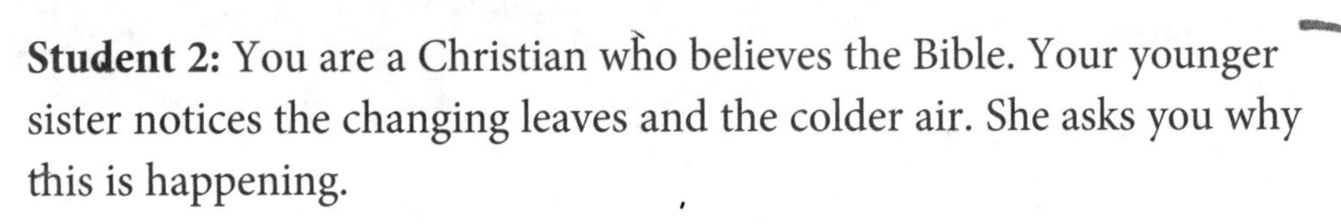

Student 2: You are a Christian who believes the Bible. Your younger sister notices the changing leaves and the colder air. She asks you why this is happening.

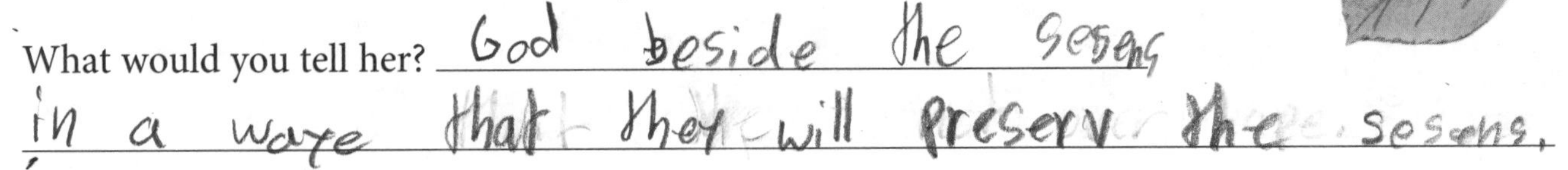

What would you tell her? God beside the sesens in a waye that they will preserv the sosons.

Can this God be trusted to care for your world? Why or why not? Yes, becuse he mad a curenet with nowa. That is he will never flud the erth.

Compare your answers with your partner's answers. They show two different worldviews.

1. Which worldview is true? The 2 student is teling the truth.
2. Why can the God of the Bible be trusted to take care of you? Becuse he died on the crost for us. And loves us.

Greek Roots

The Greeks gave us not only stories but also words. Many English words are based on Greek roots.

Study the Greek roots chart. Then match each word with the correct meaning.

Greek root	Meaning
bio	life
cracy	rule
dem	people
geo	earth
graph	write
kalli	beautiful
logy	thought (science or study)
myth	story
theo	god

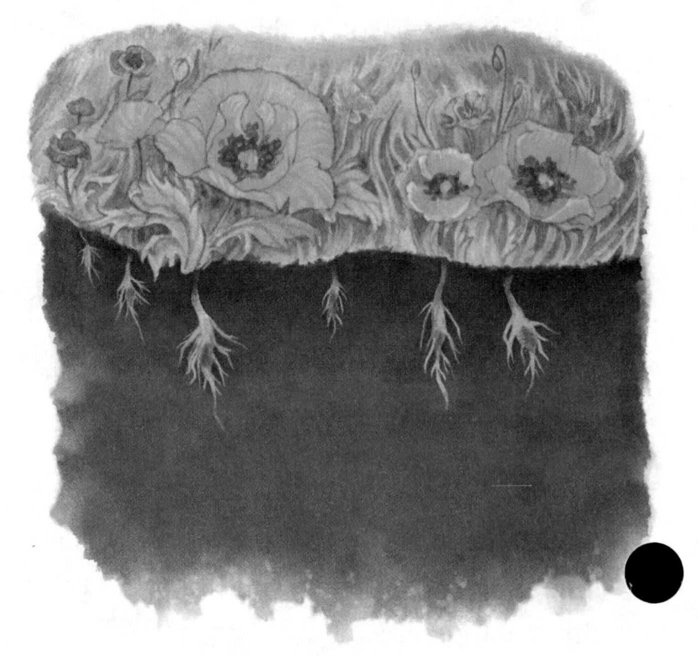

B 1. the study of life
A 2. a written work about someone's life
H 3. the study of God
E 4. the study of the earth
C 5. the art of beautiful writing
D 6. rule by the people
F 7. the study of a culture's stories
G 8. rule by God

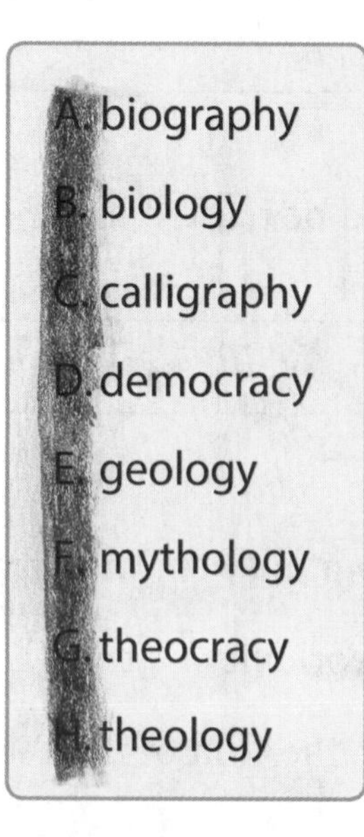

A. biography
B. biology
C. calligraphy
D. democracy
E. geology
F. mythology
G. theocracy
H. theology

Imagery

Read the poem. Follow the directions.

1. Mark the sense that enjoys the word picture of this poem.

   ○ sight ○ sound ○ taste ○ smell ○ touch

2. Underline the words or phrases in the poem that appeal to this sense.

3. List the sense that enjoys the rhythm and rhyme of any poem. ______________________

Read aloud "Twinkle, Twinkle" to a friend. Notice the rhythm, rhyme, and imagery as you read.

Answer the questions about "Something Told the Wild Geese."

4. What were the wild geese told to do? ______________________________

5. Who or what do you think told the wild geese to do this? Explain why you believe this.

   ____

   ____

Come to Your Senses

Mark the correct answer.

1. What is imagery?
   - ○ words that begin with the same letter
   - ○ words that appeal to the senses
   - ○ words that rhyme with other words

2. Why does an author use imagery?
   - ○ to help the rhythm of the poem
   - ○ to help the rhyme of the poem
   - ○ to help create a picture in the reader's mind

3. Which sentence best shows the use of imagery?
   - ○ I heard a bird chirping.
   - ○ The bluebird chirped sweetly from the rough wooden fence post.
   - ○ The bird sat on the fence post and sang.

Think of a line from a poem, nursery rhyme, or song that uses imagery. Write the line here.

4. ____

____

Write a synonym for each underlined vocabulary word.

______________ 5. The <u>luster</u> of the apple made it appear like a ruby.

______________ 6. I <u>cautioned</u> him not to go there alone.

______________ 7. The rows of apple trees in the <u>orchard</u> were perfectly straight.

______________ 8. The <u>amber</u> leaves were a blend of brown and red.

Samuel Eaton's Day

Match each genre with its description.

_______ 1. poetry

_______ 2. fable

_______ 3. myth

_______ 4. narrative nonfiction

A. tells about real-life events in an enjoyable story-like way

B. has animal characters that speak and behave like humans

C. expresses ideas and feelings, often in only a few lines

D. includes supposed gods and goddesses

Use text from *Samuel Eaton's Day* to answer the questions.

5. During what year was *Samuel Eaton's Day* written? _______________

6. What two facts about the first winter was Samuel aware of? _______________

7. What village did the Eatons live in? _______________

8. What village projects might a carpenter like Mr. Eaton have helped with? Look at the story's pictures for clues. _______________

9. What had Samuel "been longing for"? Why? _______________

Write two sentences from the story that use language from the time period.

10. _______________

11. _______________

Interpret one of the sentences chosen for numbers 10–11 by using modern-day language. Use the glossary on Student Text page 248 as needed.

12. _______________

Read this paragraph about Jackie Robinson. Change the paragraph's point of view to first person by writing it as if you yourself were Jackie Robinson. The first change has been made for you.

I

Jackie Robinson was born January 31, 1919, in Cairo, Georgia. He loved to play baseball. In 1947, Robinson signed a contract to play for the Brooklyn Dodgers. He was the first African American to play in the major leagues. His life helped further the cause for civil rights. With his help, the Dodgers won the World Series in 1955. He retired from baseball two years later.

In 1972, Robinson died in Connecticut.

Robinson signs with the major league.

Use words from the text to answer the questions.

13. What are three things Jackie Robinson is known for? ______________________

____

____

14. What group of people did the civil rights movement help? ______________________

15. How old was Jackie Robinson the year he died? Tell how you found the answer.

____

16. How does changing the text to first-person point of view make it more enjoyable to read?

____

17. In what way do the photo and caption support the text? ______________________

____

All in a Day's Work

Skim *Samuel Eaton's Day*. Record these details about the Pilgrims' way of life.

1. List the three chores that Samuel had to complete before beginning his work on the harvest. ______

2. List three hardships the Pilgrims faced when harvesting rye. (page 242) ______

3. List two other tasks that awaited Samuel after a long day of harvest. ______

Write the answer.

4. Name two characteristics that Samuel Eaton and other Pilgrims needed to survive.

5. Why was it so important to Samuel to show that he could do a day's work of harvest?

6. List the four things that Samuel prayed for. (page 247) ______

7. Why do you think prayer was important to Samuel? ______

Plan for the Future

Pretend you are a pilgrim like Samuel. You want to help your father and others by finding an easier way to fetch water, snare animals, harvest crops, or entertain the young children. Pick one chore and tell what improvements you would make with the limited supplies you have.

Available supplies: wood, straw, animal skins, stones

1. ______________________________

____

____

____

Answer using your own words.

2. What did Samuel say about complaining on page 242? ______________________________

____

3. What is meant by "done" when Samuel and Mam were talking on page 244? ______________________________

____

4. What does each person say about Samuel's work?

Sarah Morton (page 238) ______________________________

Robert Bartlett (page 245) ______________________________

____

Father (page 246) ______________________________

5. What did Samuel mean when he said, "Tis a man's hurts I am feeling"? ______________________________

____

Picture It

Illustrations in a story are important for many reasons. They help us picture the characters or events in the plot. Sometimes they create a funny or serious mood. Good illustrations always support the author's message.

Choose an illustration from *Cranberry Thanksgiving* that helps you understand more about a character or the plot. Write the page number and a sentence that explains your opinion.

Page _______

This illustration helps me understand ________________________________

____

____

Choose an illustration from *Cranberry Thanksgiving* that you think adds humor to the story. Write the page number and a sentence that explains your opinion.

Page _______

This illustration is funny because ________________________________

____

____

Work with a partner to answer the questions.

1. What is the theme of *Cranberry Thanksgiving*? ________________________

   ____

2. How do the illustrations support this message? ________________________

   ____

   ____

   ____

Draw Your Own Thanksgiving Meal

Draw a picture of your Thanksgiving table with your favorite foods on it.

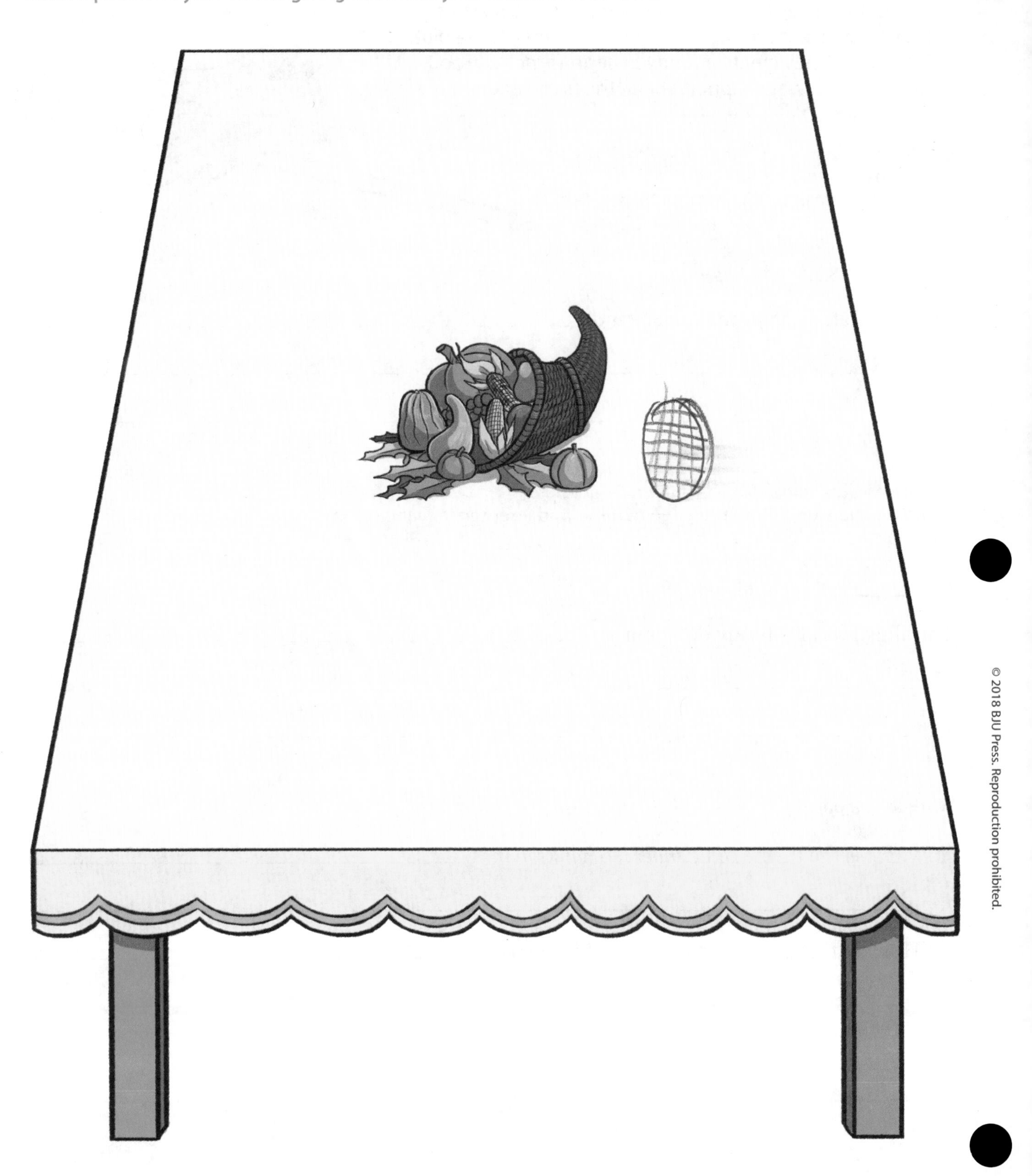

Not All Pilgrims Are the Same

Read the paragraphs. Use the information along with details from the story *Molly's Pilgrim* to complete the Venn diagram on the next page.

The Pilgrims who sailed to the New World on the *Mayflower* came from England. The laws of England said that they had to go to the Church of England. But some English Christians did not agree with all the teachings of this church. They wanted to worship God as the Bible taught. These Christians were persecuted. Pastors were removed from their churches. Some were put into prison. A group of families from Scrooby, England, decided to leave. They moved to the Netherlands to have their own church. But after a while, they became worried. They did not think the Dutch culture was good for their children. This group decided to sail to America. There they could set up their own government. They would try to make good laws that pleased God. They became known as the Pilgrims.

Not everyone comes to America for the same reasons as the Pilgrims. Some come for freedom of worship, but not the freedom to worship as the Bible teaches. Some come to be able to freely practice a false religion. Some come for other kinds of freedom. They come for the freedom to find better jobs, to receive a better education, or to live in greater safety.

Work with a partner to place each phrase in the correct part of the diagram.

- came to worship as the Bible teaches
- came to worship differently from the Bible's teaching
- came to escape persecution
- tried to make good laws that pleased God
- wanted a better job
- wanted to set up their own government
- came from England
- came from Russia

Venn Diagram

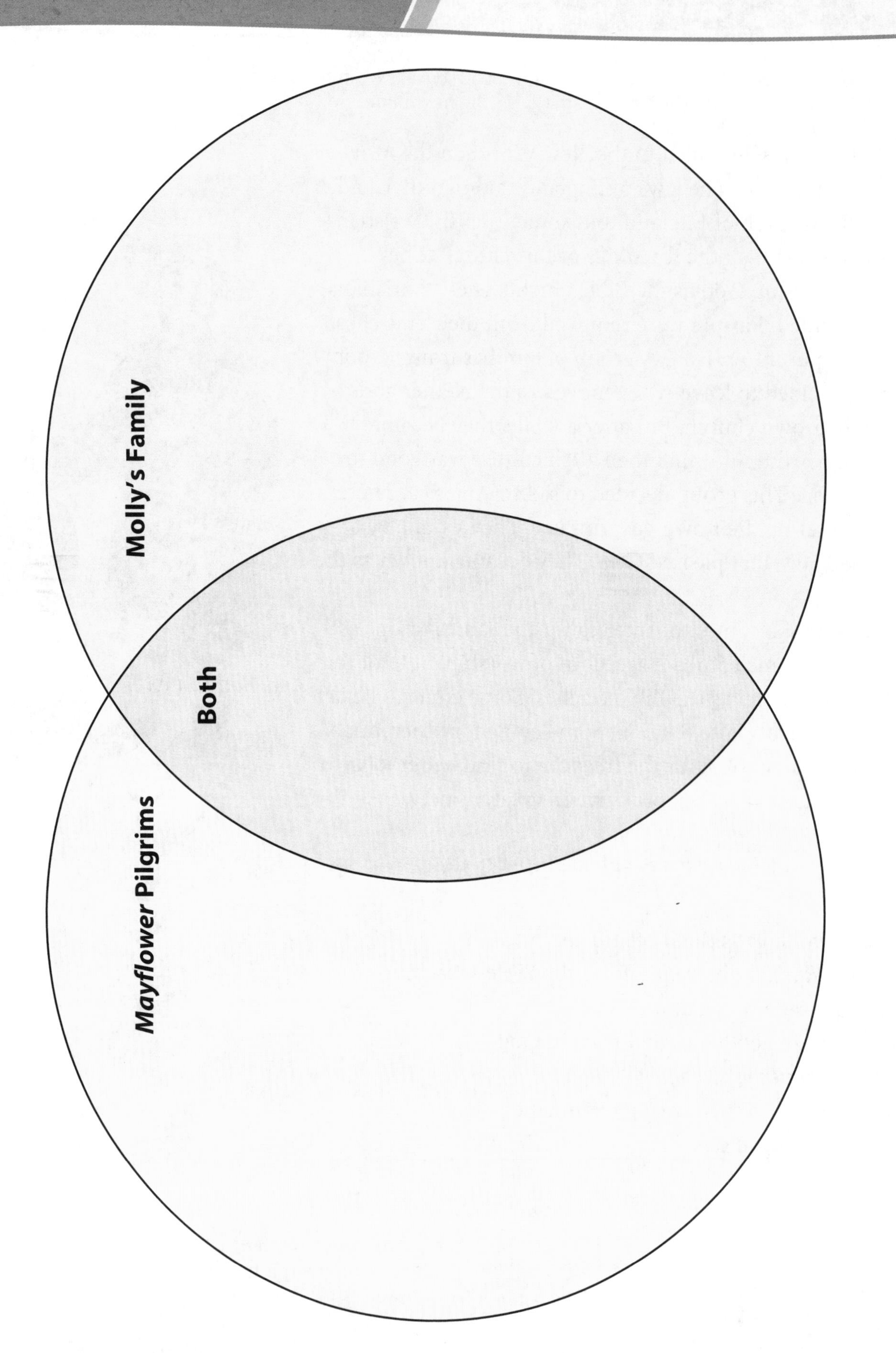

A Bleak Midwinter

Underline the words in the first stanza of the poem that describe the season as "bleak."

In the bleak mid-winter
Frosty wind made moan,
Earth stood hard as iron,
Water like a stone;
Snow had fallen, snow on snow,
Snow on snow,
In the bleak mid-winter
Long ago.

Read each question. Mark the answer.

1. What sense is used to detect moaning wind?
   - ○ smell ○ taste ○ hearing
2. What sense is used to detect the earth "hard as iron" and "water like a stone"?
   - ○ hearing ○ touch ○ taste

Explain how each title relates to the poem.

"A Christmas Carol"	"In the Bleak Midwinter"

Write your answers.

3. What makes this poem a hymn? ______________________________

   ____

4. In the last stanza the speaker gives Christ her heart. Write one action word from each verse that tells a result of giving one's heart to Christ.

   Ephesians 4:32 ______________________________

   1 John 4:19 ______________________________

Creating Pictures

A poet might choose another word for *walk* to create a particular image. Write the word next to the image it matches.

march
stomp
tiptoe
limp
stroll

1. children going quietly past a baby ____________________
2. a small child in a puddle ____________________
3. a grandma at a park ____________________
4. a band at a parade ____________________
5. an injured person ____________________

Read the questions. Write your answers.

6. What is the theme of the poem? ____

____

Psalm 40:3

And he hath put a new song in my mouth, even praise unto our God: many shall see it, and fear, and shall trust in the Lord.

7. Read Psalm 40:3. How does this verse fit with the poem? ____________________

____

Match the underlined word with its meaning.

A. cold and miserable	B. rule	C. be enough	D. provide for

_______ 8. The farmer stored grain to suffice until the next harvest.

_______ 9. The princess would one day reign in her father's place.

_______ 10. "My parents sustain me every day," said Nancy, "and that makes me grateful."

_______ 11. The weather took a bleak turn in February with a record snowfall.

Creative Flakes

Angelina

Create your own hexagonal (six-sided) paper snowflake. Follow the step-by-step directions.

Materials
1. lightweight paper
2. scissors

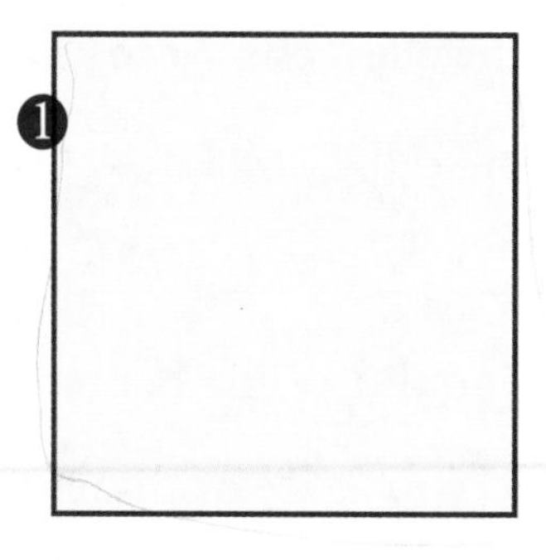

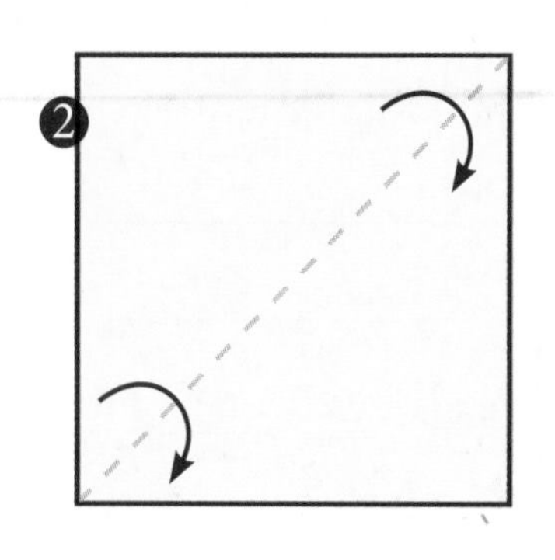

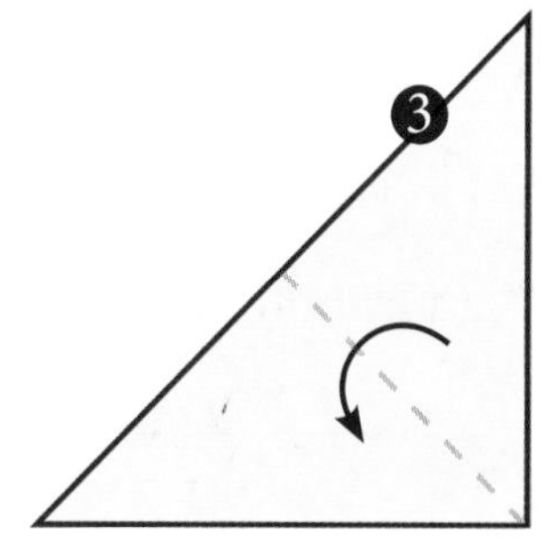

Steps

1. Begin with a square piece of paper.

2. Fold the paper in half, diagonally. The result is a triangle.

3. Fold the paper in half again. The result is a smaller triangle.

4. Fold the triangle into thirds.

5. Turn the folded paper over so that the horizontal edge is facing you. Cut off the top of the paper at an angle.

6. Keep the paper folded. Cut out creative shapes on the folded sides of the triangle.

7. Unfold the paper to reveal your six-sided snowflake!

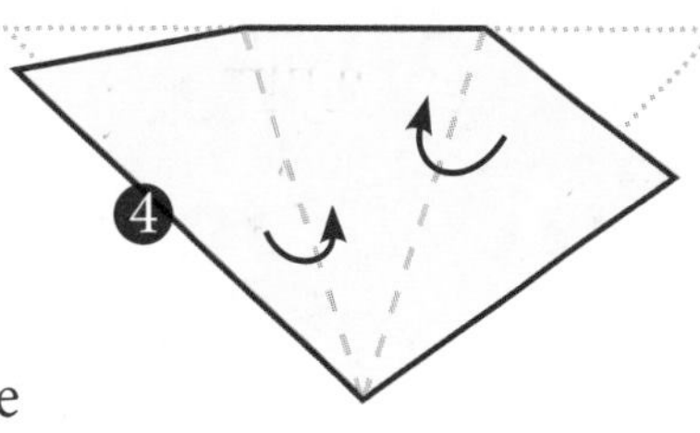

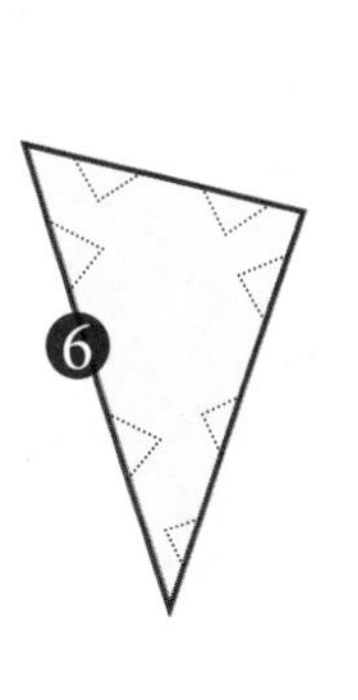

What Have You Learned?

Read the questions. Write your answers.

1. What did Willie Bentley discover as the cause for different snowflake crystals? (page 309)

 ____

2. Who did Willie Bentley say was responsible for the best snowstorm of his life? (page 310)

 Do you agree or disagree with his statement? Why? ______________________

 ____

 ____

3. Do you think snowflakes have always been as intricate as the ones Willie Bentley observed and photographed? How do you know this? ______________________

 ____

Use the Venn diagram to compare your snowflake and the snowflakes Willie Bentley photographed.

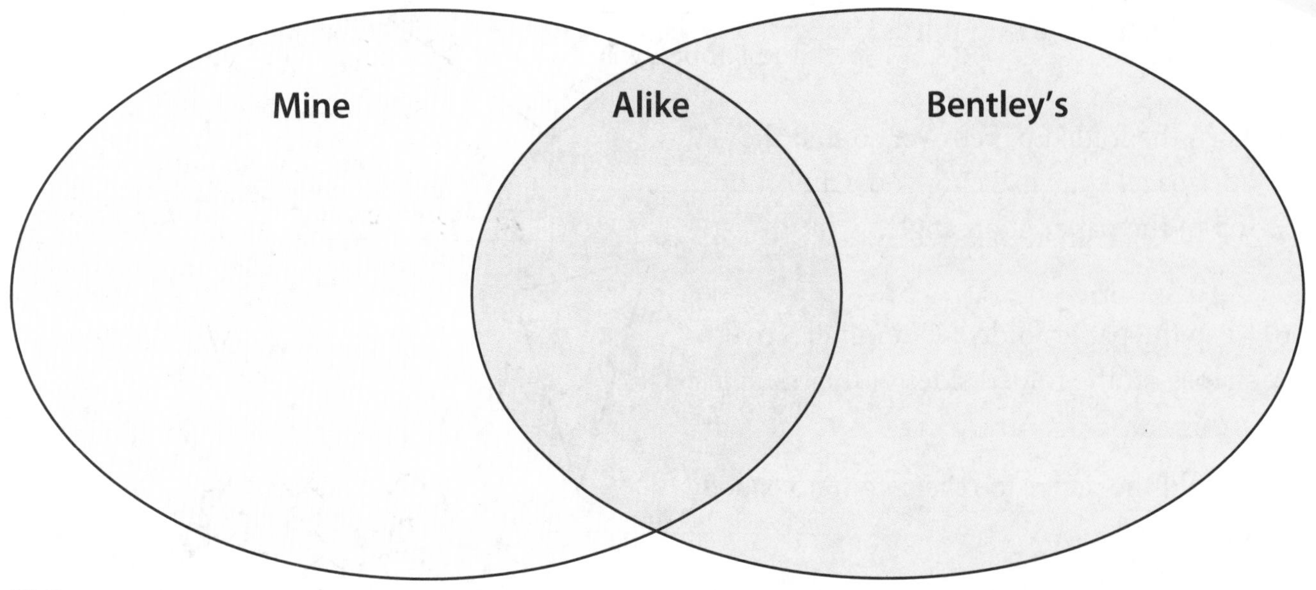

Write your answer.

4. Has your appreciation of God's design of a single snowflake changed as a result of Bentley's work? ______________________

 ____

Onomatopoeia and Personification

Complete the sentences, filling in each blank with either *Onomatopoeia* or *Personification*.

______________ is when an author uses words that sound similar to what they mean.

______________ is when an author gives human traits to things in nature or to other nonliving objects.

Write an *O* if the sentence uses onomatopoeia and a *P* if the sentence uses personification.

_____ 1. The old floor creaked every time I took a step.

_____ 2. The flowers smiled and nodded in the gentle breeze.

_____ 3. Thunder rumbled and lightning flashed across the dark sky.

_____ 4. The little boat shuddered and sobbed with each rolling wave.

_____ 5. The bees buzzed and hummed around the apple blossoms.

_____ 6. The great oak tree stood frowning as it guarded the forest path.

Write the answer.

7. Use onomatopoeia to write a sentence with the word "jingle." ______________

____

8. Use personification to write a sentence about a tree branch. ______________

____

9. What is the theme of "Wind Song"? ______________

____

Cartoon Creations

Draw cartoons showing three objects and the sounds they make (onomatopoeia).

Draw a cartoon showing a thing in nature or a nonliving object acting like a human (personification).

A Choice of Words

Imagery is the use of words to help create a mental picture. A poet's choice of words makes a clear, colorful picture in your mind.

Read the first verse of the poem "The Flying Squirrel" by Mary E. Burt. Underline the words in the poem that help to create a mental picture. Answer the questions.

Of all the woodland creatures,
The quaintest little sprite
Is the dainty flying squirrel
In vest of shining white,
In coat of silver gray,
And vest of shining white.

1. What words describe the size of the flying squirrel? ______________________

2. What words describe the fur of the flying squirrel? ______________________

Read the last sentence of the poem titled "Lincoln." Answer the question.

3. What is the symbolism of light in the last line of the poem? ______________________

____

____

Read the sentences. Match the definition with each underlined word. Place the letter in the blank.

A. reddish color	C. to slowly walk; to walk with effort
B. sincere; serious	D. to carve a design or drawing

_______ 4. Sidney was <u>earnest</u> when he spoke about the kindness of his classmates.

_______ 5. Marty wanted to <u>etch</u> his grandfather's barn on the old piece of wood.

_______ 6. "The <u>ruddy</u> leaves on the maple trees are beautiful," observed Margaret.

_______ 7. The group of campers <u>trudged</u> to their cabins after the long hike.

My Impression

Reread the poem "Lincoln." Choose either the first, second, or third stanza and draw a picture of the image that the stanza created in your mind.

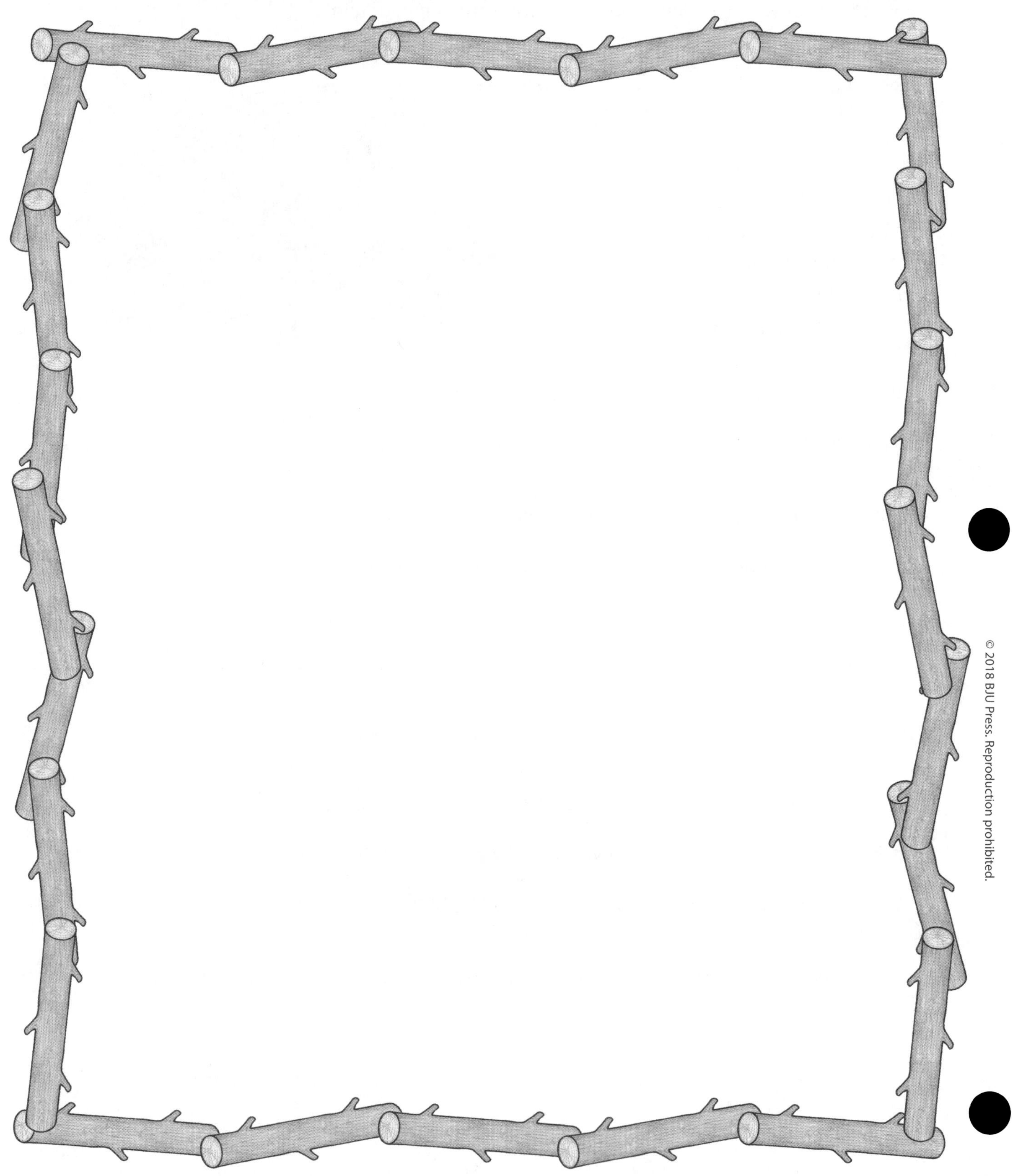

Friendly Fact Finding

Conduct an interview to obtain biographical information. Use the graphic organizer below to help you as you conduct the interview.

Biographical information about ______________________________

1. ______________________________
2. ______________________________
3. ______________________________
4. ______________________________

Appearance

1. How tall are you?
2. What color is your hair?
3. What color are your eyes?
4. Do you have any unique features?

Background

5. When were you born?
6. Where were you born?
7. What is your father's/mother's occupation?
8. How many sisters and brothers do you have?
9. What are some special memories of your early childhood?
10. Where have you lived or traveled?

5. ______________________________
6. ______________________________
7. ______________________________
8. ______________________________
9. ______________________________
____
10. ______________________________
____

11. ______________________________
12. ______________________________
13. ______________________________
14. ______________________________
____
____

Behavior

11. What is your favorite school subject?
12. What is your favorite sport?
13. What hobbies or special talents do you have?
14. What fun thing have you done recently with a relative or friend?

The Life of Someone Special

Write a short biography of the person you interviewed. Include as many details as possible to make the person "come alive."

Songs of Home

Mark the correct answer.

1. A folksong is a song ____.

   ○ about animals ○ about work ○ that belongs to a group of people

2. Where did American folksongs come from?

   ○ The British were the only ones to bring folksongs to America.

   ○ Settlers from other countries brought their homeland songs to America.

   ○ All American folksongs came from Africa.

3. Why were folksongs passed down orally?

   ○ Many common people did not know how to write.

   ○ The common people liked to hear themselves sing.

   ○ Most common people did not have paper.

Match the type of song to the people who contributed it to American folksongs.

_______ 4. British

_______ 5. western Americans

_______ 6. southern Americans

_______ 7. African slaves

A. songs about cowboys and Indians

B. songs about farms and crops

C. spirituals

D. songs about knights and nobles

Read the song "Were You There?" Answer the questions.

8. What do the verses of the song ask you to think about? ____________________

____

9. What words describe how the songwriter feels about these things? ____________________

____

10. Why do you think the songwriter chose these words? ____________________

____

____

Choose Your Words Wisely

Different groups of people sang different types of folksongs.

Read the lines from famous folksongs. Write the name of the group of people who would have most likely sung the song.

railroad workers	African American slaves	cowboys

1. As I was a-walking one morning for pleasure,
   I spied a cowpuncher a-riding along.
   His hat was throwed back and his spurs were a-jingling.

   ____

2. Swing low, sweet chariot,
   Comin' for to carry me home.

   ____

3. The switchman knew by engine moans
   That the man at the throttle was Casey Jones.

   ____

4. I've been workin' on the railroad,
   All the livelong day.

   ____

Write the vocabulary word that completes each sentence.

colonists
rhythmic
spiritual
testimony
tradition

5. A ________________ is a song that talks about religious beliefs.
6. A ________________ tune has a catchy beat and makes you want to sing along.
7. A ________________ is a statement that tells what you believe and why.
8. Most American ________________ were British common folk who settled in the New World.
9. A ________________ is something that is handed down from person to person.

Reread the lyrics of "Were You There?" Write your response.

10. On your own paper, write a five- to seven-sentence paragraph that tells your thoughts and feelings about Christ's crucifixion after reading "Were You There?"

Many Kinds of Horses

Write the correct answers in the table.

sporting horses | used for heavy work | Arabians
coldbloods | northern Europe

hotbloods		warmbloods
North Africa and the Middle East		cross between hotblood and coldblood
	Clydesdales	
small, tough horses		used for riding and competitions

Write *P* if the sentence is true of ponies. Write *H* if the sentence is true of horses. Write *B* if the sentence is true of both.

_______ 1. They are short with hairy legs and thick manes and tails.

_______ 2. They can be taller than 57 inches.

_______ 3. They are measured in *hands*.

_______ 4. One type is the Shetland.

_______ 5. One type is the Shire.

_______ 6. They can carry a grown person.

All About Horses

Write the answers.

1. List three ways horses have been used in American history.

___

___

___

___

2. List three responsibilities God has given people who own a horse. ___

___

___

___

3. How has reading this article changed the way you think or feel about horses?

___

___

Mark the correct answer. Use the Glossary as needed.

4. If a horse is shod, it is wearing ___.
   - ○ a saddle ○ horseshoes ○ a blanket
5. If a process is complicated, it is ___.
   - ○ difficult ○ interesting ○ simple
6. A mallet would be used for ___.
   - ○ sweeping ○ hitting ○ racing
7. A horse used to transport something would ___ it from one place to another.
   - ○ carry ○ drive ○ fly
8. ___ is an example of an industry.
   - ○ Hiking ○ Riding horses ○ Iron manufacturing

Horse Sense

Compare the informational text *Horses* with the story *The Black Stallion*. Work with your group to list details from the informational text that helped you better understand the story.

Rewarding Research

Think about these stories you have already read. Identify a topic in the story that you could learn more about through research.

"A Tale of Chanticleer": ______

The Cricket in Times Square: ______

Cranberry Thanksgiving: ______

Choose one topic above to research. Write three facts you learned about your topic.

- ______
- ______
- ______

Write a topic sentence you could use as the beginning of a paragraph about the topic you have chosen.

______

Speaking of Horses

Mark the meaning of the sentences written in an Old Western dialect.

1. "Some day," Pa always said, "you'll have a horse, Billy boy. When we kind of git caught up on things an' I c'n afford it."
   - ○ Pa is telling Billy he can have a horse if Billy can catch one himself.
   - ○ Pa is telling Billy he can have a horse when the family can save enough money to buy one.
2. " 'Course he ain't got no more sense'n a mule," Pa told Mr. Kingman.
   - ○ Pa is telling Mr. Kingman in a joking way that Billy is young and lacks experience.
   - ○ Pa is telling Mr. Kingman that Billy does not understand animals.
3. "Y'got a good eye fer hosses, though. I will say that."
   - ○ Pa thinks that Billy is good at finding horses hiding in the barn.
   - ○ Pa thinks that Billy knows a good horse when he sees it.

Complete the diagram.

What is the problem in the story?

____

____

What are some possible solutions?

Billy could ______________________________

____

____

Pa and Ma could ______________________________

____

____

Mr. Kingman could ______________________________

____

____

What Makes the Characters Tick?

Mark the correct answer.

1. What is Billy like?
   - ○ hardworking and obedient
   - ○ obedient but lazy
   - ○ lazy and careless

2. What was Pa like as a younger man?
   - ○ disciplined
   - ○ patient
   - ○ adventurous

3. What is Billy's attitude toward Pa?
   - ○ pity
   - ○ admiration
   - ○ disrespect

4. Why does Billy want to work for Mr. Kingman?
   - ○ to be able to save money for a horse
   - ○ to avoid having to help Pa on his ranch
   - ○ to be able to afford a new pair of boots

5. What accomplishment is Pa proud of?
   - ○ buying a large area of land for a ranch
   - ○ providing fine clothes for his family
   - ○ winning a pair of gold spurs in a rodeo

6. How does Pa wish he had been more like Mr. Kingman?
   - ○ He should have treated others more kindly.
   - ○ He should have used his money more wisely.
   - ○ He should have tried more jobs.

Mark the answer that means the same as each underlined vocabulary word.

7. The coat of the <u>sorrel</u> horse shone in the sun like flames of fire.
   ○ black ○ reddish-brown ○ golden

8. The cowboy rode the horse <u>recklessly</u> near the edge of the cliff.
   ○ without care ○ proudly ○ thoughtfully

9. The horse came from fine Arabian <u>stock</u>.
   ○ ancestors ○ barns ○ fields

Champion Stock

Write the word that completes each sentence.

actions	hints	message	words

1. Foreshadowing provides ________________ to prepare the reader for what will happen later in the story.
2. Characters in a story show their emotions through their ________________ and ________________.
3. The theme of a story is the author's ________________.

Write the letter of the emotion the character is demonstrating in the story.

A. love
B. sympathy
C. happy surprise
D. worry

_____ 4. Ma shakes her head with a sad look and tells Billy that sixteen dollars is not enough to buy the horse he wants.

_____ 5. Billy swallows when Mr. Kingman tells him he plans to sell the colt someday.

_____ 6. Billy gives up some of his savings to pay for half of Ma's dress and leaves the store with a good feeling inside.

_____ 7. Ma makes a little gasping sound and holds up the dress with tears in her eyes.

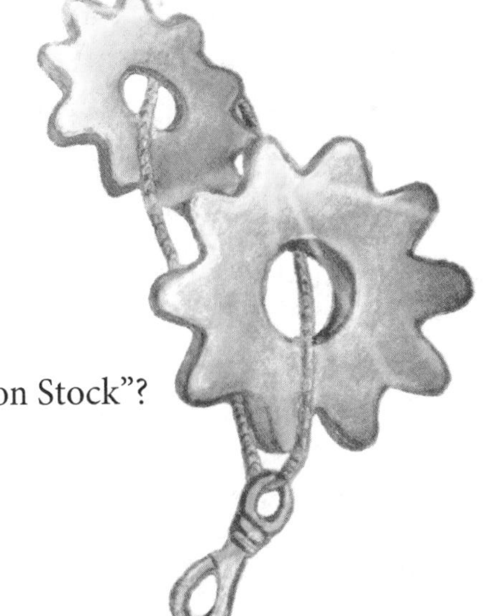

Mark the correct answer.

8. Which of the following is part of the foreshadowing in "Champion Stock"?
   - ○ a saddle
   - ○ a jewelry store
   - ○ the corral fence
9. Which is the best statement of the theme of "Champion Stock"?
   - ○ People do not always understand what we really want.
   - ○ Love motivates us to make great sacrifices for others.
   - ○ A person is sure to accomplish his goal if he works hard enough.

Mark all the correct answers for each question.

10. What does Mr. Kingman mean when he says that the colt is from champion stock?
    - ○ The colt has already won rodeos and races.
    - ○ The colt's parents or other ancestors have been champions.
    - ○ The colt is expected to be a fine horse because of its good breeding.

11. How is the title "Champion Stock" true of the human characters in the story as well as the colt?
    - ○ Billy's father is a champion rider.
    - ○ Billy's father is a "champion" at loving and sacrificing for others.
    - ○ Billy has learned from his father the value of sacrificial love.

12. What do the sacrifices in this story help us understand?
    - ○ Loving parents make sacrifices for their children.
    - ○ Christ showed His great love for us by sacrificing Himself for us.
    - ○ It is not rewarding to give up something we want for others.

Write the vocabulary word that completes each sentence.

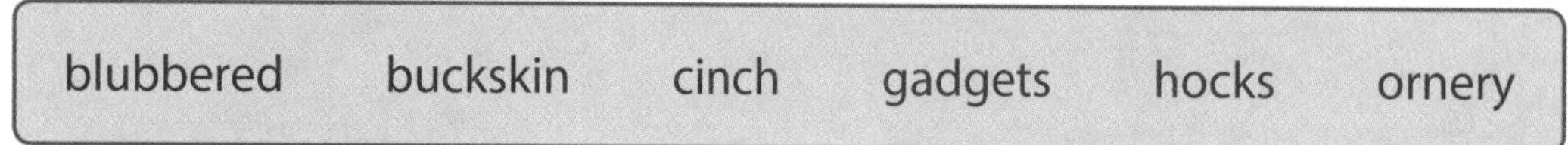

I took the lighter-colored ____________ horse out for a ride rather than the black horse. I tightened the ____________ and swung myself into the saddle. After walking in the rain, the horse had mud up to its ____________. I tried to wash off the mud, but that ____________ horse kicked over the bucket of water. The water splashed all over my little sister, who ____________ like it was the end of the world. I decided I needed to get one of those ____________ that sprays the soap and water from a distance.

Problems and Solutions

Write the answers.

1. What is the main problem in the story *The Black Stallion*? ______________________

____

2. What is the solution to this problem? ______________________

____

3. What is the main problem in the story "Champion Stock"? ______________________

____

4. What is the solution to this problem? ______________________

____

____

Mark the correct answer.

5. In *The Black Stallion*, which statement best describes the solution?
   - ○ The main character solves the problem.
   - ○ Another character solves the problem.
   - ○ The problem is solved by an unexpected twist in events.

6. In "Champion Stock," which statement best describes the solution?
   - ○ The main character solves the problem.
   - ○ Another character solves the problem.
   - ○ The problem is solved by an unexpected twist in events.

Characters in Action

Read the description of the character's actions. Write the trait that each character demonstrates as he works on the solution to the problem.

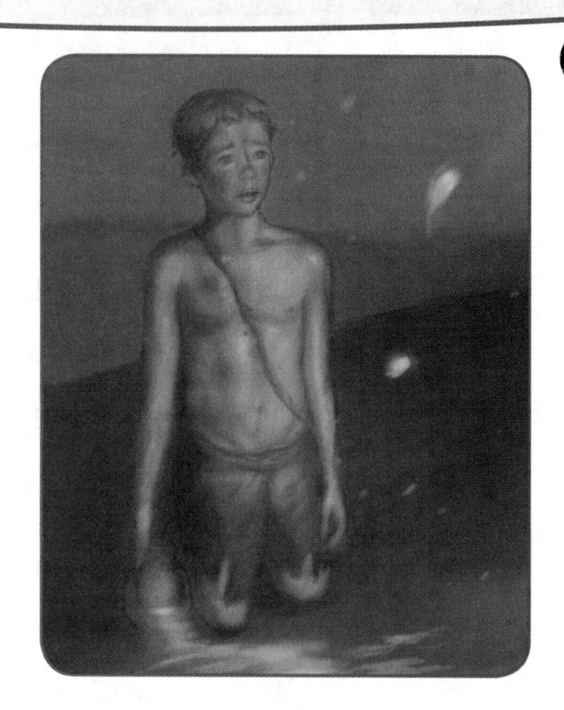

1. In *The Black Stallion*, Alec does not give up trying to solve problems. When a fire burns his shelter, he grits his teeth and thinks to himself that he is not licked yet. He goes to the beach right away to see if he can find more wood to build another shelter. However, he does not know that the solution to his main problem—how to get off the island—is already on the way.

   ____

2. In "Champion Stock," Pa sees how much Billy wants Mr. Kingman's colt. He notices how hard Billy is working to buy it. He wishes that he could help Billy buy the colt. At last he decides on a way to help Billy. But it is a solution that comes at great cost to himself, because he must give up something that he highly values.

   ____

Confess and Repent

Psalm 51 teaches a sinner to confess and repent. Psalm 51 shows the right response of a sinner toward his sin and God. The psalm also shows God's response to the sinner who confesses and repents.

Read the responses below the chart. Based on Psalm 51, write the number of each response in the correct column.

A sinner's response to God and others	God's response to the sinner

1. restores the joy of salvation
2. admits sin
3. has much mercy
4. teaches other sinners about truth
5. opens mouth and speaks praises
6. blots out sin
7. sings aloud
8. washes and cleanses completely
9. delivers from guilt
10. offers a broken and humble heart

Complete each statement about the theme of Psalm 51. Mark two correct answers for each statement.

11. When I sin, I ___.
    - ○ can earn God's forgiveness
    - ○ cannot earn God's forgiveness
    - ○ must come to God for forgiveness

12. When I confess and repent, God ___.
    - ○ wants me to be right with Him deep in my heart
    - ○ only cares about my outward behavior
    - ○ makes me clean within

Mark two correct answers.

13. What imagery in Psalm 51 pictures God's cleansing?
    - ○ purge with hyssop
    - ○ whiter than snow
    - ○ build the walls of Jerusalem

My Response

Match each underlined vocabulary word with its meaning.

A. confess	C. reject	E. sin
B. purify	D. repentant	F. woody plant with purple-blue flowers

_____ 1. To make things right with his classmates and teacher, Ben knew it was important to acknowledge his part in the locker-room fight.

_____ 2. Marco was contrite for lying to his father about the broken lawnmower.

_____ 3. The boys did not despise Gordon's offer to help them set up their tent.

_____ 4. The hyssop was used in worship by the ancient Hebrews.

_____ 5. Kelly wanted Shawn to understand the iniquity of stealing money from her mother's purse.

_____ 6. Shelly paid for Kim's broken phone to purge her guilty conscience.

Write a prayer of confession to God about the sin of lying.
Use your Bible to help you with this prayer.

Dear Heavenly Father,

____

____

____

____

____

In Jesus' name, amen.

In your private time of Bible reading and prayer at home, write a confession to God for a sin that God has revealed in your own life. Use your Bible to help you with your prayer.

And the Climax of the Story Is . . . ?

Climax is the highest point in the story. The highest point in the story is the point of greatest excitement or greatest emotion.

Recall the climax in "Word of Honor." Write the answer.

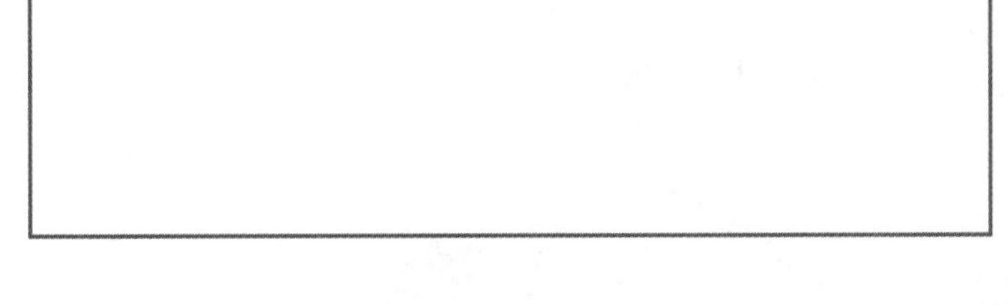

Think back to the story "Champion Stock." Identify the climax of the story from the choices provided. Write the answer.

- Billy finds out Mr. Kingman plans to sell the black colt.
- Billy spends most of his money on Christmas presents for his parents.
- Billy opens the barn door and sees the black colt.
- Billy wants to buy a horse of his own.

Rising Action

Rising action is part of a story's plot. Rising action happens as the suspense in the story increases. During rising action, the events of the story are leading up to the climax.

Label the parts of the plot diagram using the word bank.

Beginning	Climax	End	Middle

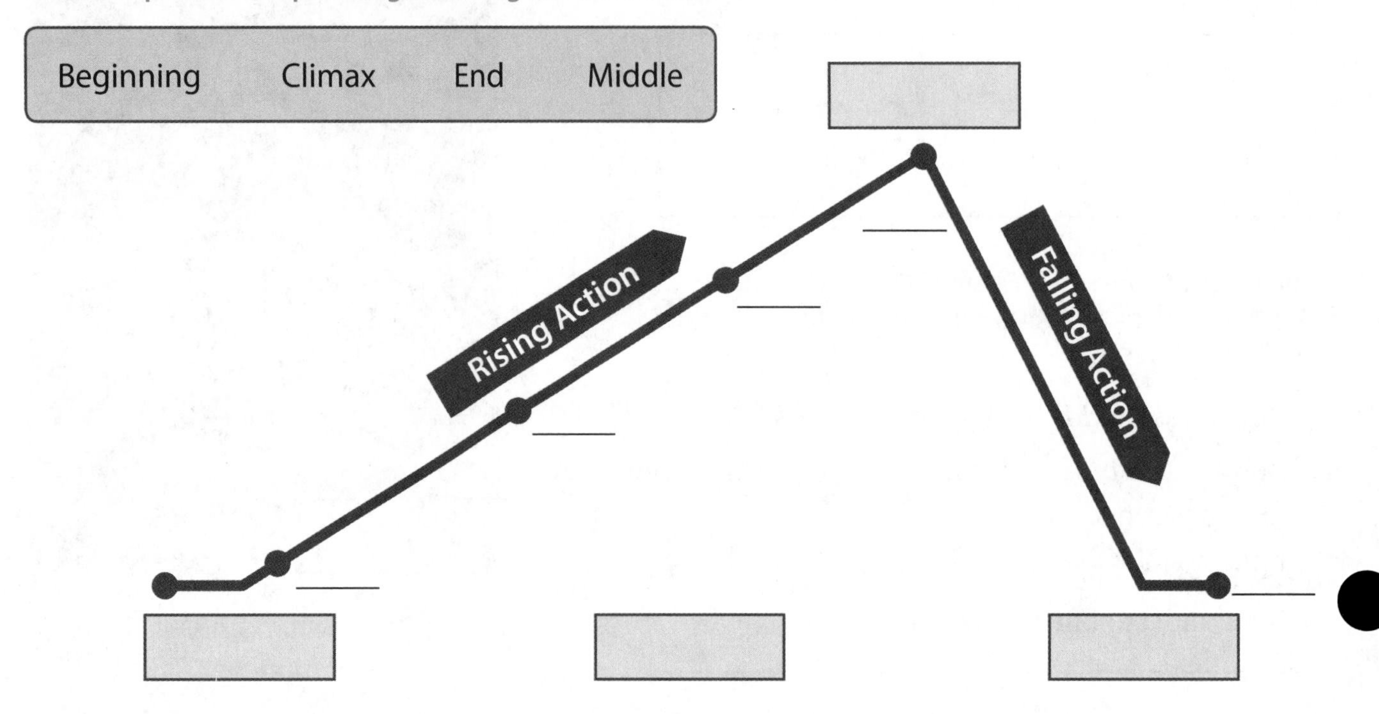

Write the letter of each story event on the appropriate line on the plot diagram. Circle the letters on the diagram that are part of the rising action.

A. "Mr. Hines? I'm ready to talk now." With his eyes on the ground, David blurted out the whole story—the lie on the permission slip, the lie to his parents, and the lie he had let all the other boys on the hike believe.

B. [Mr. Hines] had taught David's fourth-grade boys' Sunday school class. And now, just before the new school year started, he was taking them all on an overnight hike.

C. Mr. Hines stepped up beside him. "How's it going, David? You've been pretty quiet on this trip. Everything all right?"

D. A leaf blew into the fire, and David watched it shrivel and break apart in the flame. Then he bowed his head.

E. Mom smiled. "He was up late last night finishing his Bible reading," she said. "Did you get it all done, David?" David waited only a second before answering. "Yes," he said without looking up.

Taking the Gospel

John 3:16

For God so loved the world,
that he gave his only begotten Son,
that whosoever believeth in him should not perish,
but have everlasting life.

Answer the questions.

1. What is the message of the verse John 3:16?

2. Is the story "John 3:16—A True Story" realistic fiction or biography? Explain how you know.

3. Why is "A Place on the Map" a good title for the first part of "John 3:16—A True Story"?

4. Who did God provide to travel with Gladys Aylward?

5. What did Gladys and her traveling companion talk about with one another and others?

6. Reread the part of the story that talks about Gladys and her companion's prayers. Why was Gladys ashamed? (page 520)

7. How did God answer the prayer of Gladys's traveling companion?

God Answers Prayer

Mark 16:15

And he said unto them,
Go ye into all the world, and preach the gospel to every creature.

1 John 5:14

And this is the confidence that we have in him, that,
if we ask any thing according to his will, he heareth us.

Answer the questions. Write the prayers as directed.

1. In Mark 16:15, Jesus speaks to His disciples. According to the verse, who does God desire for us to share the gospel with? ____________________

2. We meet people every day. Write a prayer asking God to send someone your way to tell about Jesus. ____________________

____

3. Who has God already brought into your life that needs to hear the gospel?

____

4. What does 1 John 5:14 teach about requests made to God?

____

____

5. God desires for us to tell the gospel to others. Write a prayer asking God to help you talk about Jesus with the person you identified in number 3. ____________________

____

____

____

God Is Sovereign

Mark all the correct answers for each question.

1. How did God show His care for Gladys as she traveled?
   - ○ God provided people to serve as guides from village to village.
   - ○ God provided Gladys with a backpack of food.
   - ○ God provided Gladys with a traveling companion.

2. What unusual events did God use to introduce Himself as "the God who loves" to the lamas?
   - ○ Chinese students were burdened to pray for people in a place on the map.
   - ○ A missionary's heart was burdened to answer a prayer for someone to take the gospel.
   - ○ A man was burdened to give out tracts in a village where the monks passed through.

3. What did the Bible's command of "Go ye into all the world and preach the gospel" cause the lamas to realize?
   - ○ The lamas only had to wait.
   - ○ God would send a messenger to bring the gospel to the lamas.
   - ○ The lamas must go and tell the gospel to the Chinese.

4. What must a lama do to spend eternity with the God who loves?
   - ○ Live a life separated from the world.
   - ○ Trust in Christ who paid the price for sin and conquered death.
   - ○ Go and tell the gospel to the Chinese.

5. Sovereignty is the greatest power and authority that is given to any ruler. How do you see the sovereignty of God in the biography "John 3:16—A True Story"?
   - ○ God burdens and leads people as they seek to follow Him.
   - ○ God reveals Himself to those who seek Him.
   - ○ God provides for the needs of His children.

6. How can every believer take part in sharing the gospel with others?
   - ○ Pray for people, both those you know and those you have never met.
   - ○ Follow the Holy Spirit's prompting.
   - ○ Leave your home and travel to China to tell others of God's love.

God Is Love

Read 1 Corinthians 3:6–9.

Paul is talking about how he and Apollos followed God's leading to take the gospel to the people in Corinth. They planted and watered the seed of the gospel, and God gave the increase.

Reread the head lama's story as he told it to Gladys on Student Text pages 526–28. Complete the flow chart to tell who had a part in bringing the gospel to the lamas.

Who planted the seed of the gospel?

Who watered the seed of the gospel?		

Who caused the seed of the gospel to take root and grow in the hearts of the lamas?

Write the vocabulary word from the story.

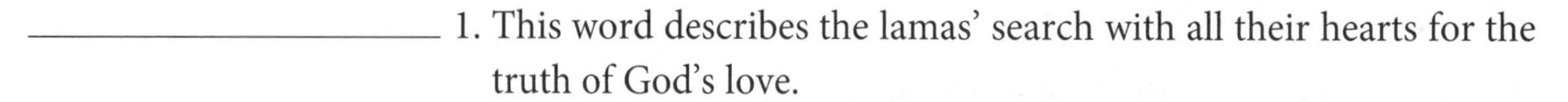

_______________ 1. This word describes the lamas' search with all their hearts for the truth of God's love.

_______________ 2. This word describes how the lamas accepted the gospel.

Hymn Imagery and Theme

"When I Survey the Wondrous Cross" describes Jesus' death on the cross. Isaac Watts chose vivid images to show how Jesus suffered. The hymn also gives a personal response to the death of Jesus.

Underline the word or words in the hymn that create a vivid picture in your mind.

Stanza 1

When I survey the wondrous cross
On which the Prince of glory died,
My richest gain I count but loss,
And pour contempt on all my pride.

Stanza 2

Forbid it, Lord, that I should boast,
Save in the death of Christ my God!
All the vain things that charm me most,
I sacrifice them to His blood.

Stanza 3

See from His head, His hands, His feet,
Sorrow and love flow mingled down!
Did e'er such love and sorrow meet,
Or thorns compose so rich a crown?

Stanza 4

Were the whole realm of nature mine,
That were a present far too small;
Love so amazing, so divine,
Demands my soul, my life, my all.

Write the last two lines of the hymn in your own words to explain the theme.

"Love so amazing, so divine, / Demands my soul, my life, my all."

____

____

Read Galatians 6:14. Write your answer.

How does "When I Survey the Wondrous Cross" reflect this verse? ______________________________

____

____

Wondrous Freedom

Read the story. Match each vocabulary word with its meaning.

The guard shoved the prisoner forward. "He's no good, Captain," said the guard with contempt. "He tried in vain to escape his chains, but I put an end to that!" The guard jabbed the prisoner with his elbow.

"Good work, soldier," said the captain. He saluted the guard in approval.

"Please, sir," begged the prisoner. "Please let me go! I cannot live in prison! I must be free!" Tears mingled with his cries for mercy.

The captain surveyed the prisoner, who had fallen to his knees. "I'm sorry, but granting freedom to a traitor is not in the realm of my authority. You will have to take it up with the general."

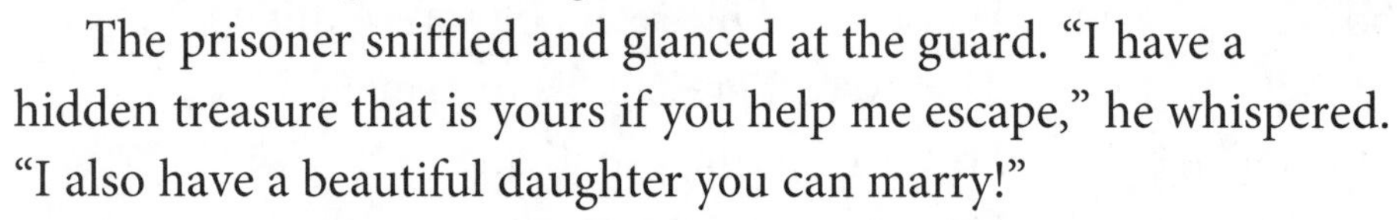

The prisoner sniffled and glanced at the guard. "I have a hidden treasure that is yours if you help me escape," he whispered. "I also have a beautiful daughter you can marry!"

The guard frowned and shook his head.

"See, soldier?" said the captain, who had heard the prisoner's desperate offers. "Freedom is a wondrous thing! This man is willing to do anything to be free! Now, let's be off. The general shall decide this prisoner's future."

A. contempt	C. realm	E. vain
B. mingled	D. surveyed	F. wondrous

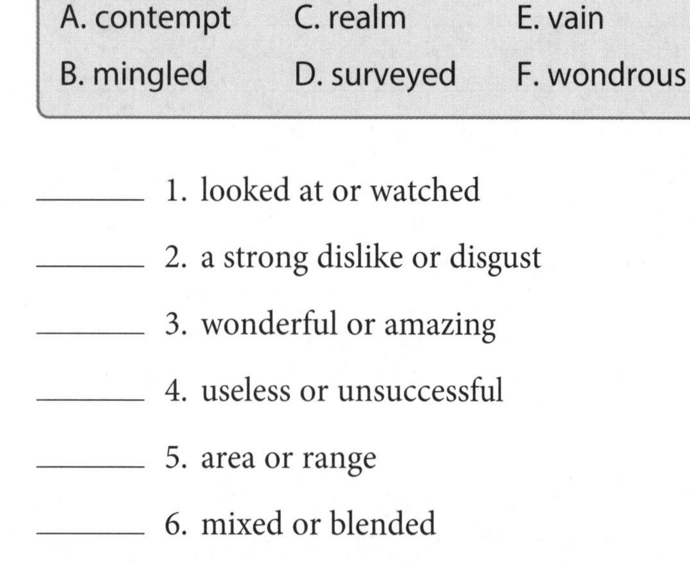

_______ 1. looked at or watched

_______ 2. a strong dislike or disgust

_______ 3. wonderful or amazing

_______ 4. useless or unsuccessful

_______ 5. area or range

_______ 6. mixed or blended

The Gospel

Read the Bible verses with a partner. Match each reference to the truth it gives about the gospel.

A. Matthew 28:5–6	C. John 14:16–17	E. 2 Corinthians 5:21
B. John 3:16	D. Romans 10:13	F. Titus 2:14

_______ 1. Jesus rose from the tomb and is living today.

_______ 2. Jesus gave Himself so that He could redeem mankind.

_______ 3. Jesus was the perfect, sinless sacrifice for our sins.

_______ 4. People who call on the name of the Lord shall be saved.

_______ 5. The Holy Spirit comes to dwell in those who believe in Jesus.

_______ 6. Jesus' death allows all who believe in Jesus for salvation to spend eternity with Him.

Mark the correct answer.

7. Who responded with "I'll go" and set out two days later on foot to take the gospel to unreached villages in China?

   ○ Gladys Aylward ○ Isaac Watts ○ the monks in China

8. Who responded to Christ's sacrificial love by wanting to give "soul," "life," and "all" to Him?

   ○ Gladys Aylward ○ Isaac Watts ○ the monks in China

9. Who responded to John 3:16 with amazement and faith that God would send a messenger to further explain God's love?

   ○ Gladys Aylward ○ Isaac Watts ○ the monks in China

My Response

Think about why Jesus died on the cross. He suffered and died for you! Are His death and resurrection meaningful to you? How does it make you feel to know that God loves you so much that He sent His Son to die for you? Isaac Watts, Gladys Aylward, and the Chinese monks all responded to the gospel in clear ways. How do you respond to the gospel?

What does the gospel mean to you? Write a paragraph describing your own response to the gospel.

Think about how Isaac Watts, Gladys Aylward, and the Chinese monks responded to the gospel. How did you feel when you read about their responses? What did their responses make you want to do?

Write a paragraph describing the effect their responses had on you.

Foreshadowing and Story Conflict

Reread Student Text page 534. Write three examples that foreshadow what may happen later in the story.

1. ______________________________

____

____

____

____

____

Write *T* if the statement about story conflict is true.
Write *F* if the statement is false.

_______ 2. A character can experience different conflicts at the same time.

_______ 3. Conflict describes something as larger or more interesting than it really is.

_______ 4. A conflict states a comparison directly, using the word *like* or *as*.

_______ 5. A story's conflict can change as the plot develops.

_______ 6. Conflict is the type of struggle an author uses to draw the reader into the story.

_______ 7. Conflict is a word that describes what a person or animal is like.

Write the type of conflict shown in the examples from *The Cabin Faced West*.

man vs. man	man vs. self	man vs. nature	man vs. machine

_______________ 8. This is no ordinary storm. The rain and wind pound Ann and the others as they try to gather corn in the cornfield.

_______________ 9. Ann is not sure she wants to spend the winter in Gettysburg with her cousin, Margaret. Should she ask her parents? She has always wanted to go back, but now she feels confused.

Conflict and the Main Character

Write the answers to explain one conflict Ann faces.

Man vs. Self	
Ann's reasons for returning east to Gettysburg:	Ann's reasons for staying in the West at Hamilton Hill:

Write your answer.

1. Predict whether Ann decides to return to Gettysburg or to stay at Hamilton Hill.

____

Read the vocabulary word in the shaded box. Underline the word or words in each sentence that mean the same thing.

peculiar — 2. The boy had a strange look on his face after tasting a tuna and peanut butter sandwich.

fierce — 3. The lion walked back and forth in his cage and gave a powerfully strong roar that made everyone at the zoo jump in fright.

ragged — 4. The hem of my skirt was torn unevenly after it got caught in the car door.

crier — 5. The announcer stood on the palace steps, reading the king's new law that required every citizen to pay more taxes.

streaked — 6. Water moved quickly down Mom's clean window after we hit it with water balloons.

The Cabin Faced West

Write the answers.

1. Explain how the storm is a symbol in the story. ______________________________

____

____

____

2. Explain how the cabin is a symbol in the story. ______________________________

____

____

Mark all the correct meanings of the title *The Cabin Faced West*.

○ The Hamiltons miss Gettysburg because they are too far west of it.

○ The Hamilton cabin sits on a hill and looks west.

○ Like the cabin, the Hamilton family is facing west and will not return east to Gettysburg.

○ The Hamilton family does not like the fierce western storms.

○ The Hamilton family is moving forward into a new life and will not look back because they believe God led them to the "Western Country" and will watch over them there.

Write the answers.

3. Explain why your prediction about Ann's decision to leave or stay was correct or incorrect. ______________________
____

4. How does the conflict of man versus self end?
____
____
____

5. How does the conflict of man versus nature end?
____
____
____

Match the vocabulary word to the sentence it completes.

A. battered	C. flimsy	E. seeped
B. blur	D. loft	F. tattered

_______ 6. We climbed the ladder to the ___, where we will sleep during our camping trip.

_______ 7. Dad held up his ___ coat and stared at our dog, who sat in the corner with his head down.

_______ 8. While I was spinning around on the carnival ride, everyone in the crowd became a ___.

_______ 9. Because the thin cardboard box was too ___, it fell apart as soon as we climbed into it.

_______ 10. Water ___ into our tent during the heavy rain, and all of our gear got wet.

_______ 11. The hurricane winds ___ the small boat.

Fact or Opinion?

Match each feature of the *Our Farm* selection with its purpose.

_______ 1. helps explain a photograph

_______ 2. gives additional information that helps the reader understand the main text

_______ 3. breaks up information and helps the reader find the main idea

_______ 4. helps the reader visualize the information

A. section title
B. caption
C. photo
D. sidebar

Write *F* in the blank if the statement is a fact.
Write *O* in the blank if the statement is an opinion.

_______ 5. My favorite color is green because it is the prettiest.

_______ 6. The color green is a blend of yellow and blue.

_______ 7. Red, yellow, and blue are known as primary colors.

_______ 8. I think yellow is a good color for the kitchen walls.

_______ 9. I prefer my blue T-shirt over my red one.

_______ 10. My baseball uniform is blue and white.

_______ 11. I do not think uniforms should be white because they get dirty easily.

_______ 12. The best color for a uniform is red.

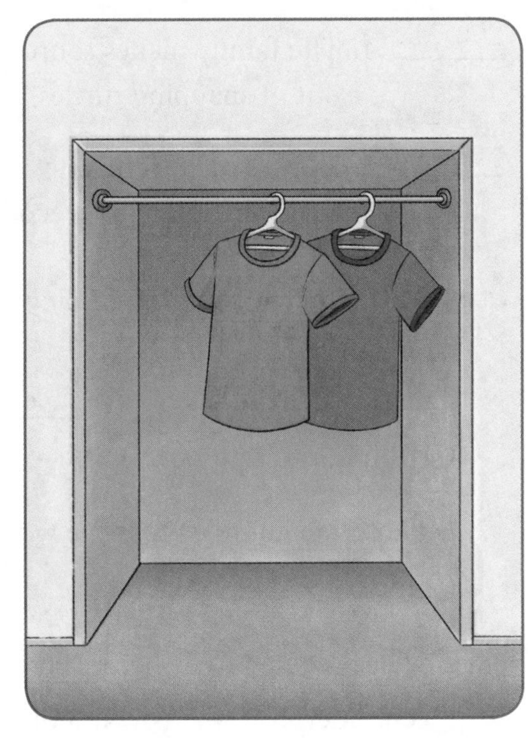

Complete each definition.

13. A fact is something _______________ to be true.

14. An opinion is a _______________ that is not supported by knowledge or proof.

Demonstrating Design

Match each fact from *Our Farm* with the truth it shows about God's purpose and design in His creation.

_______ 1. The family hears coyotes talking to one another at night.

_______ 2. The family often finds nests in the pinecone trees.

_______ 3. The family does not see owls because they are out only at night.

_______ 4. The family makes soup out of snapping turtles.

_______ 5. Turtles often return to their birthplace to breed.

A. God gave humans dominion over animals, and He gave us animals to use for food.

B. God gave animals the ability to communicate with each other.

C. God gave some animals instincts that allow them to find their way back to a familiar place.

D. God made some birds with the ability to see and hunt their prey in the dark.

E. God designed many animals with the knowledge of how to create their own homes.

Mark the choice that gives the meaning of each underlined word. Use the Glossary as needed.

6. America's Great Lakes have diverse resources, including many different species of fish.
   - ○ only a few
   - ○ various
   - ○ many of the same kind

7. My internal compass tells me we are going north even though I can't see the stars.
   - ○ inner
   - ○ dependable
   - ○ visible

8. The bee seemed to be flying aimlessly among the flowers, never landing to gather nectar.
   - ○ confidently
   - ○ without a goal
   - ○ very slowly

9. Coral reefs provide habitats for animals such as sponges, fish, mollusks, and worms.
   - ○ special food
   - ○ warm water
   - ○ unique living places

10. Will the hikers be able to orient themselves by the sun's position in the sky?
    - ○ get one's bearings
    - ○ hide from
    - ○ set on fire

Favorite Places

Read the interview and answer the questions.

Jessica: Our family homeschools because we do a lot of traveling. My dad is a construction manager, and he goes to different job sites for several months at a time. We come with him in our motor home.

Jason: I think it's fun to see different parts of the country. We have lived in seven different states, and I'm only ten!

Jessica: I think the best part of the country is the West. We lived in Arizona for a while. I love the cacti, and Arizona has more beautiful sunsets than any other state in the country.

Jason: I don't agree with my sister that the West is the best place to live. I like Florida best because I love the beach.

1. Who are the two speakers being interviewed? ____________________
2. What is the relationship between them? ____________________
3. Why does their family homeschool? ____________________
4. What is one fact given in the interview? ____________________

   ____

   ____

5. What is one opinion given in the interview? ____________________

   ____

   ____

Write one fact and one opinion about a place where you have lived or visited.

Fact: ____________________

____

Opinion: ____________________

____

Something's Fishy

Use information from *Our Farm* to mark all correct answers for each question.

1. What are some reasons God has designed fish to eat other fish?
   - ○ to satisfy their need for food
   - ○ to destroy the balance between fish and plants in a pond or lake
   - ○ to keep one kind of fish from becoming too plentiful

2. Why is it not wrong for people to catch fish?
   - ○ God has created fish to be good for food.
   - ○ Catching fish can control the fish population in a pond or lake.
   - ○ Fish are not as important to God as other animals.

Use the roots and prefixes to find word meanings. Mark the correct answer.

Latin Prefixes:
re—again; back
pre—before
ex—out of
con—together
at—to; toward
de—away; from

Latin Roots:
tract—to pull, draw, or drag
serv—to save or keep

3. Use that fishing lure to attract catfish to your line.
   ○ draw toward ○ keep away ○ keep together
4. Let's reserve some of the chocolate cream pie for dessert tomorrow.
   ○ pull away from ○ keep back ○ drag out again
5. Mom used tweezers to extract the splinter from my finger.
   ○ pull out of ○ pull again ○ save back
6. Wear sunscreen to preserve your skin and to avoid sunburn.
   ○ keep together ○ pull away ○ keep as before
7. I think those tall statues detract from the view of the garden.
   ○ draw attention away ○ save as before ○ save together
8. As mud dries, it contracts and causes cracks in the earth's surface.
   ○ keeps away ○ pulls out of ○ pulls together

Lost and Found

____

Mark the correct answer.

1. A narrative poem ___.

   ○ always rhymes ○ is written in paragraphs ○ tells a story

2. All poetry, including narrative poems, ___.

   ○ expresses ideas and feelings ○ uses rhyme ○ tells a story

3. The poem "Lost and Found" ___.

   ○ is not meant to be humorous

   ○ reveals truth in an everyday experience

   ○ is written in free verse

4. "Lost and Found" brings out an important theme about ___.

   ○ prayer ○ helping others ○ being responsible

Write the correct answers about the poem "Lost and Found."

5. Characters: ______________________________

6. Setting: ______________________

Number the events of the plot in order.

_______ Speaker finds his father on his knees, muttering.

_______ Father checks the dresser drawer.

_______ Speaker suggests that his father ask God for help.

_______ Father begins to laugh.

_______ Father loses his keys.

_______ Father looks under the sofa.

Lost and Found

Use vocabulary words from *Our Farm* and "Lost and Found" to complete the crossword puzzle. Consult the Glossary as needed.

Across

2. beyond what is normal or needed
3. draw toward
8. protection of natural resources

Down

1. help or aid
4. unique living place
5. one who feeds on another creature
6. inner
7. keep in a specific condition

How I Helped

Write a paragraph about a time you helped someone. Remember to include specific details that create a mental picture.

My Narrative Poem

Break your paragraph into lines to create a free-verse narrative poem. To keep the poem brief, you may choose to use only portions of your paragraph. Use line breaks where there are natural breaks in thought or where new sentences begin. Draw a picture to illustrate your poem.

Descriptive Details

If the statement is true of an autobiography, write *A*. If the statement is true of a biography, write *B*. If the statement is true of both, write *AB*.

_______ 1. story about a real person's life

_______ 2. story that shares personal memories of one's own life

_______ 3. story written about a person's life by another person

_______ 4. nonfiction story

Authors add descriptive details to make the setting come alive.

Match the plain words with the author's descriptive words.

Plain words	Descriptive words
_______ 5. white house	A. "endless tall grass that billowed in the wind like the waves of an ocean"
_______ 6. moving prairie grass	B. "stacks of golden brown loaves"
_______ 7. drying wash	C. "brilliant jars of deep red beets . . . and delicious, rosy watermelon pickles"
_______ 8. bread	D. "trudge back and forth over the little wooden bridge, bringing back pail after pail of rainwater from our 'moat'"
_______ 9. carrying water	E. "sweet-smelling sheets and clothes flapping in the sun"
_______ 10. canned vegetables and fruit	F. "little white ship at sea"

Write the answers.

11. Write the letter of the quote from above that you like best. _______________

12. Why do you like that quote best? _______________

____

13. Explain how the author's words help you to sense the prairie. _______________

____

The Best Choice Is . . .

Write the word that best completes each sentence.

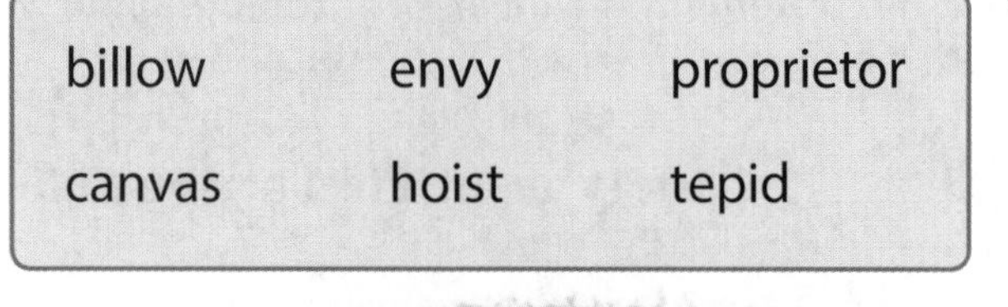

1. It was hard for the prisoner not to ____________________ the guard's steak dinner as he ate his own scrap of bread.
2. The ____________________ water that Carlos drank after his soccer game did not cool him off.

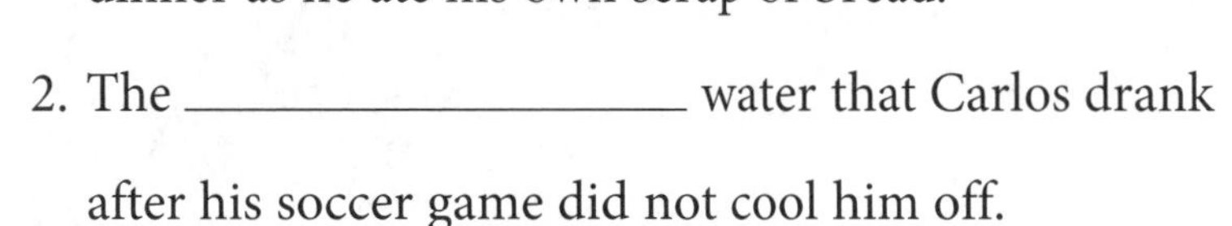

3. "____________________ the sails," yelled the captain of the ship. "We need to get this vessel underway!"
4. Can the large ____________________ sails of the ship stand up to the heavy rain and strong wind of the storm?

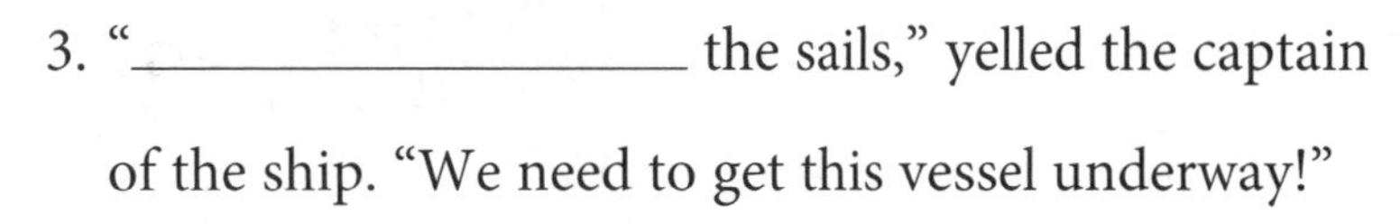

5. As soon as Esther would hang the soft white sheets on the clothesline, they would ____________________ in the warm breeze.
6. "I am the ____________________ of this candy store," Teddy told his brother. "And I want every child to receive a free piece of candy on the Fourth of July."

Compare the stories *Dandelions* and *My Prairie Year* by completing the Venn diagram. Write each letter in the appropriate section of the diagram.

A. traveled by railroad
B. home is built of sod
C. western pioneers
D. family is hardworking
E. traveled by covered wagon
F. home is built of pine boards

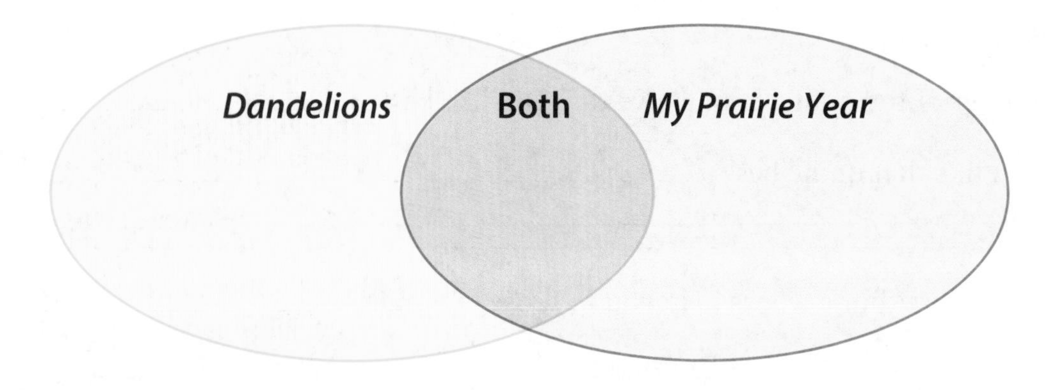

Traits and Responses

Mark the traits that would be most beneficial for a pioneer.

○ fearfulness	○ hard worker	○ adventurer	○ laziness	○ courage
○ responsiblity	○ good neighbor	○ flexiblity	○ weakness	○ unfriendliness

Write the answers.

1. Which one of Elenore's character traits impressed you the most? ____________________
2. How did she show this trait? ______________________________

____

Fill in the blank with Elenore's response to each experience.

important	homesick for Maine	disappointed
cried	too terrified to scream	

3. When Elenore discovered the wagon train was a mirage, she felt ____________________.
4. Because of the cold during the first winter, Elenore ____________________.
5. When Elenore was surrounded by a wall of prairie fire, she was ____________________.
6. When Elenore spent her tenth birthday driving a grain wagon, she felt ____________________.
7. When Aunt Addie's package arrived, Elenore felt ____________________.

Read Philippians 4:6. Write the answer.

8. According to Philippians 4:6, what are the proper responses for a Christian to have to any situation in life, such as the situations that Elenore faced? ____________________

____

Suitable Words

Read the paragraph. Answer the questions. Use the Glossary as needed.

After the storm, Jane and Tilly raced boisterously to the camp ball field. Everyone was excited about the enormous cookout that was planned for after the game. Tilly laughed when she thought of the last cookout. Jane had scorched her hot dog. Then she had burned several marshmallows to a crisp. It was incredible to think that their week at camp was nearly over. Tilly tapped Jane urgently on the shoulder. She wanted to remind Jane to be careful during the cookout. Jane did not respond. She stood frozen, staring at something. Then Tilly noticed what her good friend was staring at. Her eyes were transfixed on a huge snake that was sunning itself on home plate.

________________ 1. Which word means "demanding immediate attention"?

________________ 2. Which word means "huge"?

________________ 3. Which word means "held motionless"?

________________ 4. Which word means "roughly and noisily"?

________________ 5. Which word means "burned on the surface"?

________________ 6. Which word means "unbelievable"?

Compare the mother in *My Prairie Year* with the mother in *Dandelions*.

My Prairie Year	*Dandelions*
Mother feels ____________	Mother feels ____________
Mother feels this way when she ____________	Mother feels this way when she ____________
____________	____________
____________	____________
____________	____________

A **timeline** organizes key events in history. It shows these events in the order they happened. It also shows the amount of time that passed between events. A timeline can help us understand how one event relates to another.

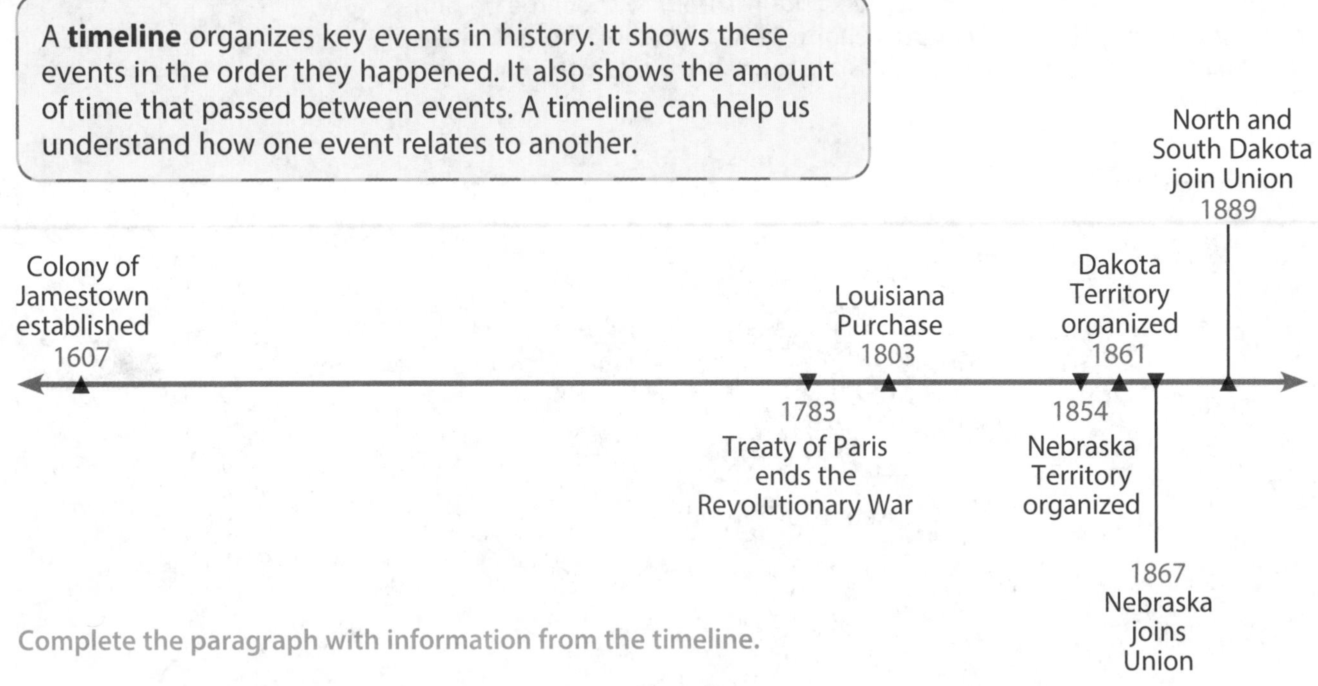

Complete the paragraph with information from the timeline.

American Expansion

In ____________________ the British established the colony of Jamestown in the New World. The colonies declared their independence from Great Britain in 1776. They fought a war to change their government. In 1783 the ____________________ ended, and America signed the Treaty of Paris with Great Britain. This treaty added much new land to the United States. Thomas Jefferson purchased the Louisiana Territory from France in ____________________. America expanded again as a result of the Louisiana Purchase. In ____________________ the Nebraska Territory was organized from the Louisiana Purchase. In 1861 the ____________________ was organized. Nebraska joined the Union as the thirty-seventh state in ____________________. The Dakota Territory was later split in two. In ____________________ North Dakota and South Dakota were added to the Union as the thirty-ninth and fortieth states.

Pioneer Travels

Draw a red line from Illinois to the Nebraska Territory to show the possible route traveled by the family in *Dandelions*. Draw a blue line from Maine to the Dakota Territory to show the possible route traveled by the family in *My Prairie Year*.

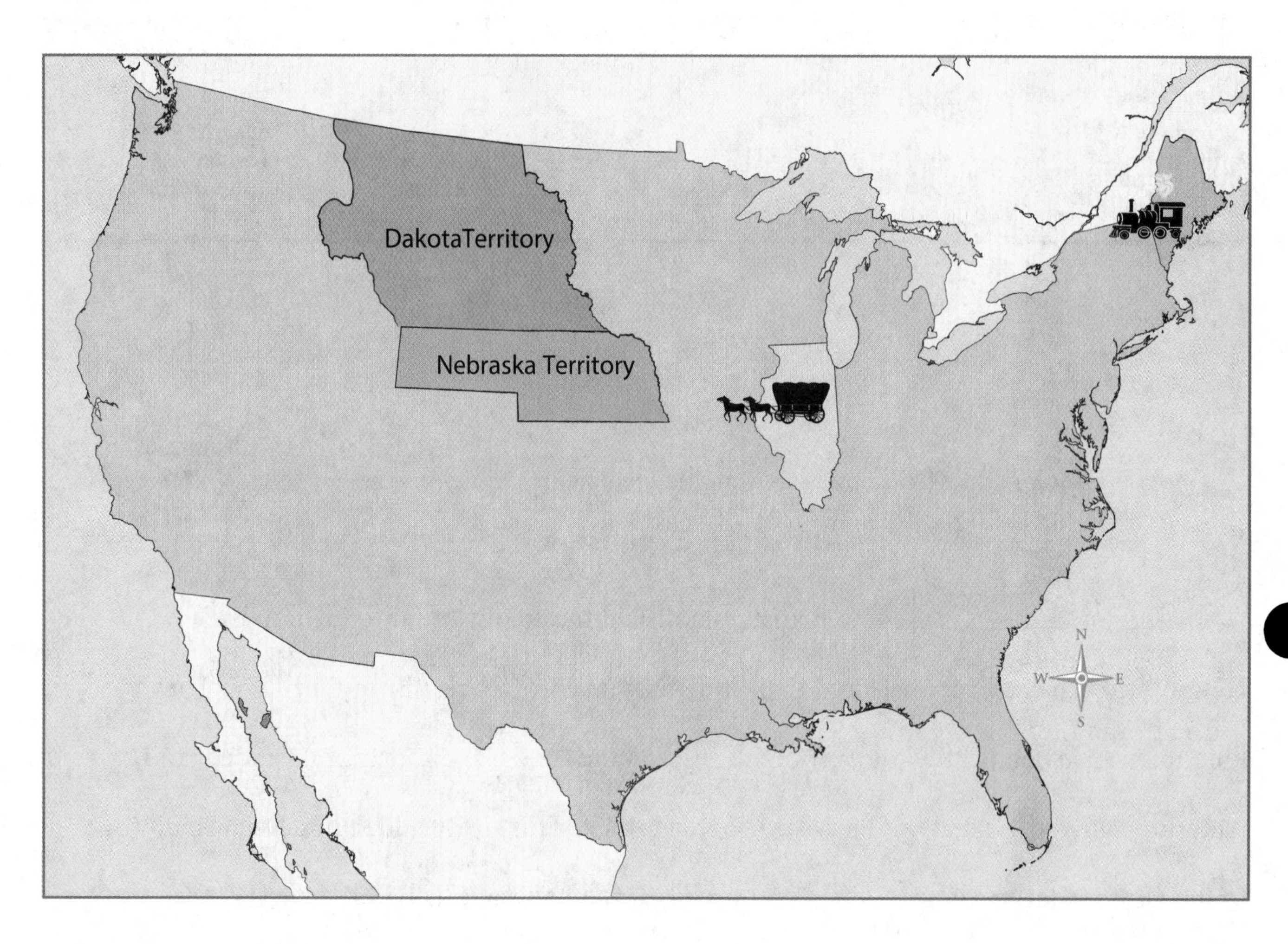

Mark the correct answer.

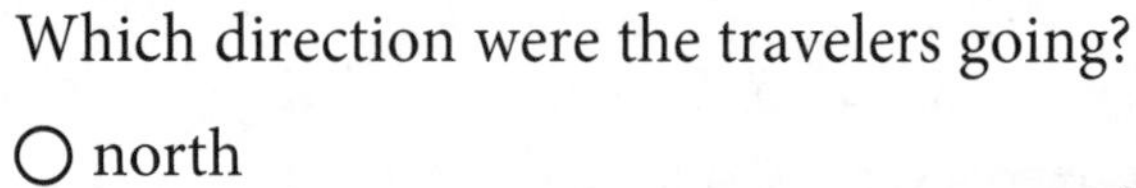

Which direction were the travelers going?

○ north

○ south

○ east

○ west

Lincoln Family History

Conduct an online keyword search of "Abraham Lincoln family tree." Select a family tree that shows at least four generations, beginning with Lincoln's grandfather, who is also named Abraham Lincoln. The family tree will need to include the date of birth and date of death for each family member shown.

Complete each statement using the information from Abraham Lincoln's family tree.

1. In what year was Lincoln's grandfather, Abraham Lincoln, born? __________
2. How old was Lincoln's grandfather when he died? __________
3. Who was older, Lincoln's grandfather or his grandmother? __________
4. How many years older was this grandparent than the other grandparent? __________
5. What was Lincoln's grandmother's name? __________
6. How many years did Lincoln's grandmother live after the death of her husband? __________
7. How old was Lincoln's grandmother when she died? __________
8. What were the names of Lincoln's parents? __________
9. In what year was Abraham Lincoln born? __________
10. Whom did Abraham Lincoln marry? __________
11. In what year was Lincoln's wife born? __________
12. How many children did Abraham Lincoln and his wife have? __________
13. How many girls and how many boys did the Lincolns have? __________
14. How old was Edward Baker Lincoln when he died? __________
15. How old was Abraham Lincoln when he died? __________

Family History in the Bible

Write the name of the person described. Use the Bible verses to help you.

_______________ I am the father of Boaz. (Ruth 4:21; Matthew 1:5)

_______________ I am the mother of Boaz. (Matthew 1:5)

_______________ I married Boaz. (Ruth 4:13)

_______________ I am the son of Boaz. (Ruth 4:21; Matthew 1:5)

_______________ I am the grandson of Boaz. (Ruth 4:22; Matthew 1:5)

_______________ I am the great-grandson of Boaz. (Ruth 4:22; Matthew 1:6)

_______________ Boaz and King David were my earthly ancestors. (Matthew 1:17)

Complete the family tree using the people identified above.

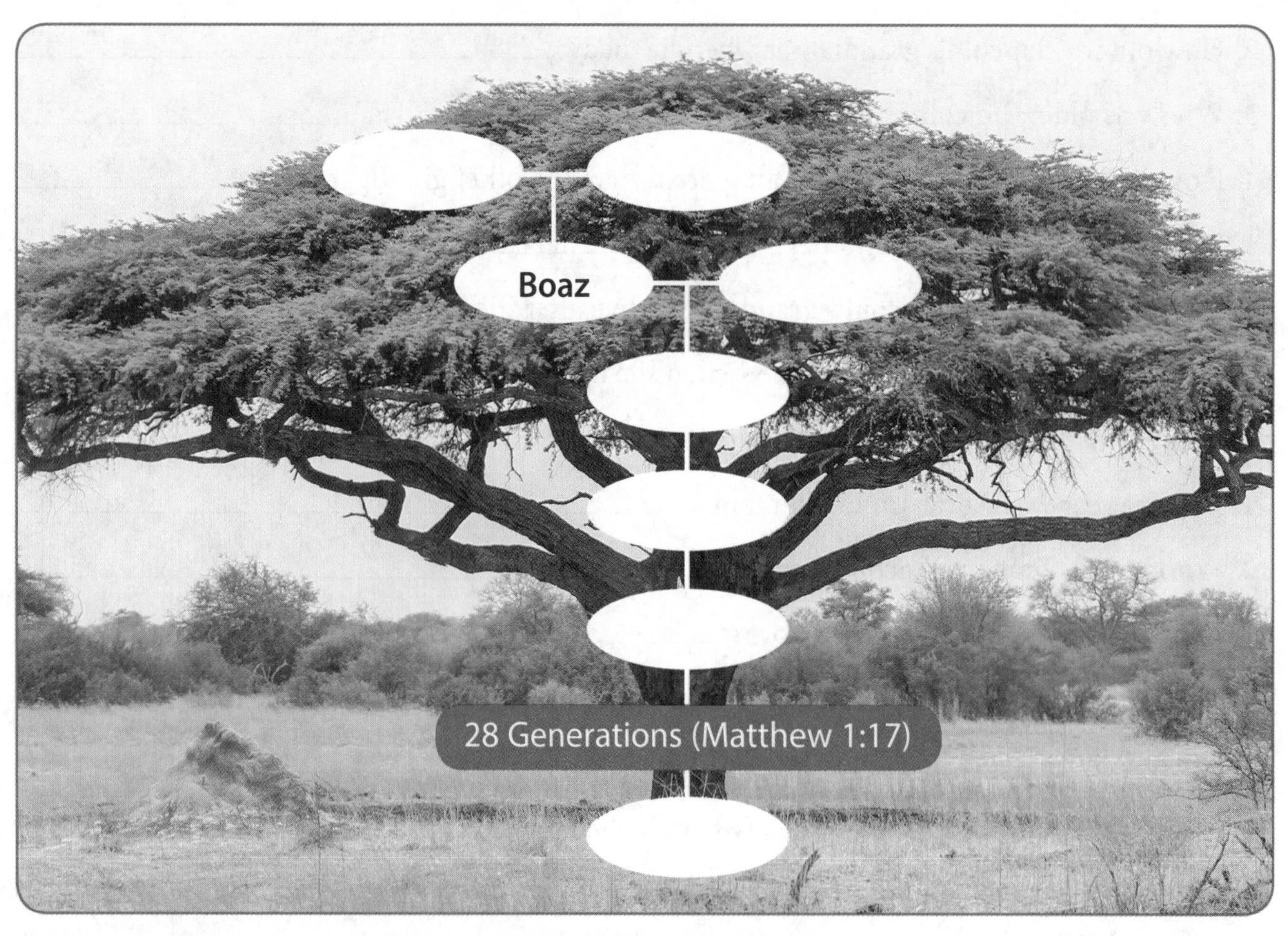

Conduct an online keyword search of "Boaz to David family tree."
Compare several online family trees to the tree you completed above.

Family Tree

Research family history about yourself, one of your ancestors, or a famous American. Find information online or by interviewing a parent, grandparent, or another older family member. Create a family tree from this research.

Person I am researching (full name): ______________________________

Date of birth: ______________ Date of death (if applicable): ______________

Website(s) visited or person(s) interviewed: ______________________________

____

____

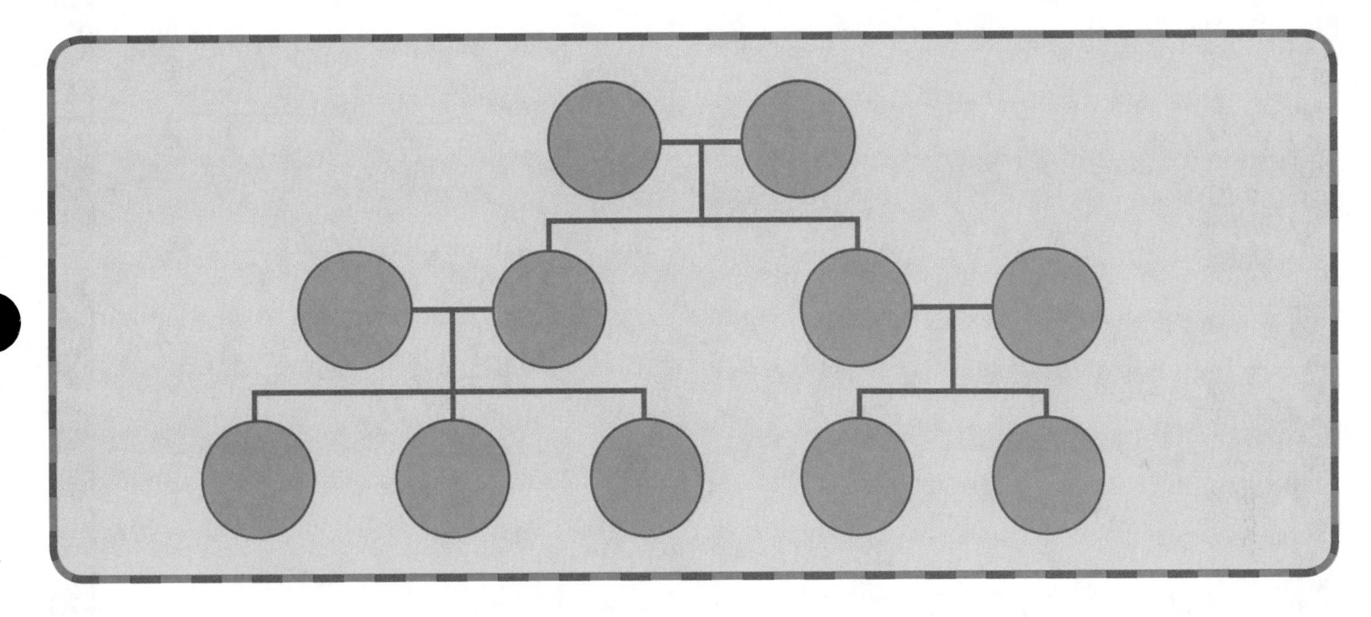

Family History Checklist

_______ 1. Research online and/or interview people to find information.

_______ 2. Draw a blank family tree on Worktext page 228.

_______ 3. Fill in the family tree with at least three generations.

_______ 4. Include the first, middle (if known), and last names of each person identified.

_______ 5. If the person is still alive, provide his year of birth (born–).

_______ 6. If the person has died, provide his years of birth and death (born–died).

_______ 7. Place the names of all individuals on the tree in their proper birth order, from ancestor to descendant.

Family Tree

for

____

A Fiery Brand

Write the genre by the feature for which it is known.

biography	fable	informational text	reader's theater	tall tale

__________ 1. teaches a moral

__________ 2. has a larger-than-life hero

__________ 3. is read from a script with character parts

__________ 4. gives details about a real person's life

__________ 5. provides nonfiction facts about a subject

Write the letter to match the effect to its cause.

Cause

_____ 6. Mr. Wesley realized his house was on fire.

_____ 7. Young John did not hear the commotion; his father could not reach him because of the flames.

_____ 8. The Wesley family had prayer time, six hours of school, and an hour of Bible reading each day.

_____ 9. John felt he must try to do as much good as he could.

_____ 10. After his father's death, John was left with an empty feeling in his heart.

Effect

A. Two neighbors rescued six-year-old John from the upstairs nursery.

B. John readily agreed to go with his brother Charles to America to preach to the Indians.

C. John chose to stay in London working on the streets instead of taking over the church at Epworth.

D. Mr. Wesley awoke his wife and the nurse.

E. John was a good student, an eager reader, and a lover of the Bible.

The Inward Witness

Number the quotations in the order that they were said in the story.

_______ "Father, I must stay in London. Drunkenness, robbery, and slave trading are all too common here. I must try to do as much good as I can."

_______ "You have been accepted at the Charterhouse School in London."

_______ "John Wesley, surely you are a brand plucked from the burning."

_______ John's father whispered, "The Inward Witness—that is the strongest proof of Christianity."

_______ "Son, your mother and I have tried to give you the best education possible."

Use Student Text page 582 and the Bible verse to answer the questions.

1. John tried to live in a way that pleased the Lord for eight years. What types of things did he do? _______________

____

____

2. What was John Wesley missing even though he did all these good works? _______________

____

3. What does the Bible say in Ephesians 2:8–9 about working for your salvation? _______________

____

Write a synonym for each underlined vocabulary word.

_______________ 4. The commotion of the passing parade kept the baby awake.

_______________ 5. The missionary gave a commentary on each picture in his presentation.

_______________ 6. Grandmother's hands were idle for only a short time before they picked up her knitting needles.

_______________ 7. The firefighters endured the fierce heat for hours.

John Wesley: A Fiery Brand

____

Write the letters of two events that occurred in each period of John's life.

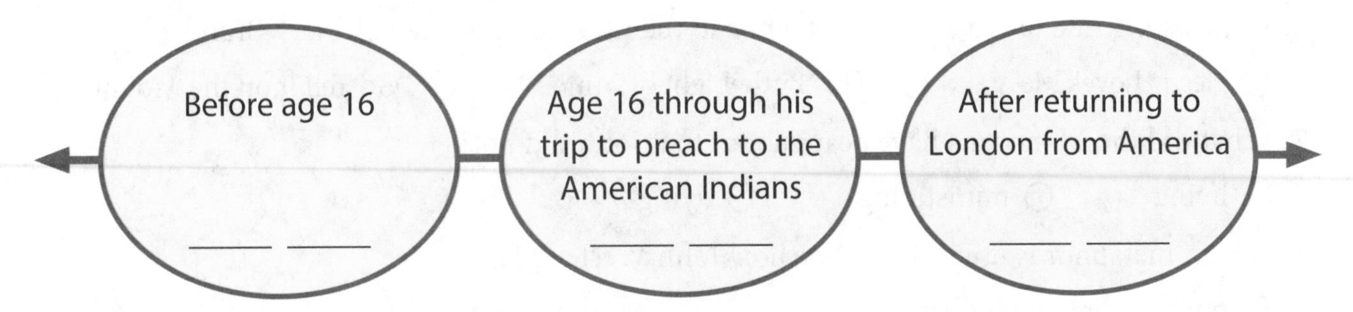

A. John heard that sinners are saved by faith in the blood of Christ alone.

B. John learned from his parents that real, living faith is tested every step of the way and that God is faithful.

C. After his father's death, John was left with an empty feeling in his heart.

D. John remembered his mother's words that "idle hands and minds are the devil's workshop."

E. John found that "the Inward Witness is the Holy Spirit, dwelling in our hearts by faith in Christ."

F. John observed that the Moravians were at peace to die, yet he was unwilling to die.

Write the answer.

1. List three events that led to John Wesley's conversion. _______________

____

____

Match the people with their responses to John Wesley's conversion.

_______ 2. John's mother

_______ 3. the English people

_______ 4. new converts

_______ 5. a mob

A. called John and his new converts "heretics"

B. acted in anger and seized John

C. copied their leaders, doing good works and living holy lives

D. wrote, "I have a great and just desire that all your sisters and brothers should be saved."

John Wesley: A Fiery Brand

Mark the correct answer.

6. Which song title uses a similar metaphor to the title "John Wesley: A Fiery Brand"?

   ○ "Jesus Loves Me" ○ "This Little Light of Mine" ○ "Go Tell It on the Mountain"

7. What did the Moravians have peace about that John did not?

   ○ living ○ ministering ○ dying

8. Which metaphor is used to describe how John Wesley's faith grew?

   ○ burning fire ○ raging storm ○ soaring eagle

9. What caused John's brother Samuel to describe him as a fanatic following his conversion?

   ○ John preached the gospel with zeal.

   ○ John was a fan of sports.

   ○ John lived in an attic.

10. Why were the people converted under John's preaching called heretics?

    ○ They did not have a church.

    ○ They became part of the Moravian Church.

    ○ They believed something that was not accepted by the religious people around them.

11. What country was transformed by John Wesley's faithful service to God?

    ○ America ○ England ○ France

12. In what way was John Wesley's life "a fiery brand"?

    ○ God used his burning zeal to lead many others to true faith in Christ.

    ○ God made him a preacher in a large church in London.

    ○ He was burned at the stake for his preaching.

Check with the Bible

Explain how the verse supports or contradicts John Wesley's thinking.

1. John hoped to save his soul himself. (John 14:6) ______________________________

____

____

2. "I must try to do as much good as I can." (Isaiah 64:6) ______________________________

____

____

3. John still believed that his good works could save him. (Ephesians 2:8–9) ______________________________

____

____

4. John found that the Inward Witness is the Holy Spirit, dwelling in our hearts by faith in Christ. (Romans 8:6–9, 15–17) ______________________________

____

____

On a separate sheet of paper, write about your conversion or the conversion of someone you know.

Work or Worship?

Read the Bible verses and mark the two correct answers for each question.

1. What does the Bible say in Titus 2:11–14 about a person's good works?
   - ○ Good works can earn salvation.
   - ○ Good works are a result of the teaching of God's grace.
   - ○ Good works show Christ's purifying work in the believer.
2. What does John 15:20 say about the response of unbelievers toward converted believers?
   - ○ The people of this world will treat Christ's followers as they treated Him.
   - ○ The people of this world will treat Christ's followers with kindness.
   - ○ Christ's followers should not be surprised when unbelievers mistreat them.
3. How did John Wesley's beliefs change to reflect the truth of Romans 10:3–4, 9–10?
   - ○ John believed he needed to work harder for his salvation.
   - ○ John believed that God alone was righteous.
   - ○ John confessed Jesus with his mouth and believed on Him in his heart.
4. How did John Wesley's converted life show the truth of Romans 1:16 and John 14:27?
   - ○ John had a peace that he did not have before.
   - ○ John was not ashamed to preach the gospel with zeal.
   - ○ John traveled to foreign countries to preach with new zeal.

Increase Mood

Write the mood each sentence creates.

anger	concern	fear	sadness

__________ 1. Josh waved the fiery end of the broken branch in the faces of the hungry wolves.

__________ 2. Josh wondered if the majestic wolf could safely cross the frozen river.

__________ 3. Josh ran his rough hand slowly over the coarse fur of the wounded old wolf.

__________ 4. Josh yelled at the top of his lungs and ran straight at the wolf that had attacked his brother moments before.

Rewrite each sentence. Add details to create the specified mood.

5. Jane held the baby chimp. (love) __________

6. Peter looked at the snake. (boldness) __________

7. The ape smelled something in the air. (curiosity) __________

Answer the questions.

8. What challenges might Seth face as a first-time pony express rider? __________

9. What mood does the author create in the first part of "Night Ride to River Station"? Explain your answer. __________

Historical Fiction

Write an *X* to mark the answer in each column.

1. Which feature in each column is true of historical fiction?

______	past setting	______	only real people	______	only facts
______	present setting	______	only made-up characters	______	only made-up details
______	future setting	______	both real people and made-up characters	______	both facts and made-up details

Mark the best answer.

2. What do an author's fictional details add to the story?

   ○ historical facts ○ excitement and interest ○ understanding

Write the vocabulary word that completes each sentence.

clumsily	crumpled	express	fidgeted	gravelly	harmonica

3. The tune from Jim's ________________ floated on the breeze.
4. The ________________ path crunched under Mr. Frank's boots.
5. The boy ________________ tripped over the misplaced log.
6. The unironed laundry laid in a ________________ heap.
7. The old goat ________________ nervously in the barnyard.
8. When Mom is in a hurry, she goes through the market's ________________ checkout.

Analyze Details

Write the answers.

1. Name three challenges that Seth faced on his first pony express ride. ______

2. Copy one of the author's sentences from "Night Ride to River Station" that appeals to your emotions. ______

3. Describe the specific details the author uses to increase emotion in the sentence you chose.

4. What kind of words add details that appeal to the emotions? ______

List one event from each part of the plot in "Night Ride to River Station."

Rising action: ______

Climax: ______

Falling action: ______

PONY EXPRESS

UNITED STATES MAIL

Mark the character's words that tell you something about his worldview and what he values.

○ "These horses aren't to learn on," Mr. Thompson had said. "Don't want to teach them bad habits that might cost a rider his life someday."

○ "You've been doing a man's work for the last few days. Your pa will be proud of you."

○ Seth asked the Lord's blessing on the food and then prayed for his father and for the pony express rider on his way to their station.

○ He mumbled something about bandits near Muddy River.

○ His mother ran to the door and hugged him tightly. "The Lord be with you, Son." She let him go.

○ "Lord, please don't let me fall and lose the horse," Seth prayed. "Help me!"

○ "Ho, Station Master!" Seth galloped into the station yard.

Write the word that completes the analogy.

aspen	crumple	distrustful	heave	relief	solitary

1. *Friend* is to *trustworthy* as *foe* is to ________________.
2. *Axe* is to *chop* as *shovel* is to ________________.
3. *Soda can* is to *crush* as *paper* is to ________________.
4. *Flower* is to *rose* as *tree* is to ________________.
5. *Scream* is to *fear* as *sigh* is to ________________.
6. *People* is to *crowded* as *person* is to ________________.

Accurate Facts

Historical facts make a story believable. An author of historical fiction often includes real people and events from the past that are important to his topic.

Mark the fact that helps to make "Night Ride to River Station" believable.

1. Stores and family homes served as ___ along the pony express route.
   - ○ inns ○ relay stations ○ restaurants
2. The pony express route between stops was often very ___.
   - ○ long ○ dangerous ○ rocky
3. A *mochila* is a ___.
   - ○ leather pouch that fits easily over a saddle and secures the mail
   - ○ leather covering for the leg that is worn over trousers
   - ○ leather strap that is used to direct the horse
4. Pony express riders rode ___.
   - ○ only during the day to avoid animal attacks
   - ○ only at night to avoid enemy attacks
   - ○ during the day or night
5. News of ___ reached California by way of the pony express.
   - ○ the battle at Gettysburg
   - ○ the attack on Fort Sumter
   - ○ the death of President George Washington
6. The pony express rider must have confidence in ___.
   - ○ his horse's sure-footedness
   - ○ his map-reading abilities
   - ○ his understanding of the weather

Verify Facts

Often a historical-fiction story can leave you wondering which details are historical facts and which details were added by the author to increase mood or interest.

Research to find the answers to the following questions about the pony express.

1. Was there really a place called Devil's Slide along the pony express route? ______________________

2. Where would a pony express rider place the *mochila*? Draw a picture or describe it in words.

3. What name was used for the locking pockets on the *mochila* that held the mail? __________

4. What book was distributed to each pony express rider? ______________________

Write the answer in your own words.

5. Explain how an author's research is important to making a historical-fiction story enjoyable.

6. On your own paper, write a question that you have after reading "Night Ride to River Station." Research your question and write the answer.

God's Creation

Write the letter to match God's activity with each day of the Creation week.

Day	Activity
_______ 1	A. God created the sun, moon, and stars.
_______ 2	B. God created light and separated day and night.
_______ 3	C. God rested.
_______ 4	D. God created land and plants.
_______ 5	E. God created birds and sea animals.
_______ 6	F. God separated the waters into ocean and clouds.
_______ 7	G. God created land animals, man, and woman.

Write the answers.

1. What made people different from the rest of God's creation? ______________________
2. From what did God form the man? ______________________
3. From what did God form the woman? ______________________
4. Name three responsibilities God gave the man and the woman. ______________________
5. What one thing did God command man not to do? ______________________

God's Creation

Write the character trait of God that is shown in each of His actions.

all-powerful	faithful to provide	good	holy

God created the world and everything in it by speaking. God is

__________________.

God's world was perfect and sinless. He commanded man not to eat of one tree. The penalty for disobedience was death. God is

__________________.

God

God looked back on what He had made each day and called it good. God is

__________________.

God gave the man the companion he needed to keep him from loneliness and to help him rule the earth. God is

__________________.

Mark the synonym of the underlined word.

6. When I look in the mirror, I see an <u>image</u> of myself.

   ○ likeness ○ difference ○ painting

7. The eggs began to hatch, and our flock of chickens <u>multiplied</u> overnight.

   ○ divided ○ died ○ increased

8. Dad sprayed weed killer to <u>subdue</u> the weeds growing in the garden.

   ○ conquer ○ help ○ improve

9. Cold sandwiches would be more <u>suitable</u> for a summer picnic than hot soup.

   ○ tasty ○ fitting ○ messy

Out of the Pea Pod

____

Write the correct word in each blank to complete the definition.

A myth is a ________________ story often used to explain a culture's beginnings or events in ________________. The actions of ________________ or ________________ in a myth affect people's lives. Many ________________ of the world have created their own myths.

Mark the correct answer.

1. "The Pea-Pod Man" offers an explanation for ___.
   - ○ the seasons ○ the creation of humans and animals ○ the problem of sin
2. "The Pea-Pod Man" is a myth from the ___ culture.
   - ○ East African ○ Greek ○ Eskimo
3. The creator in this creation myth is ___.
   - ○ a raven ○ a man ○ both a raven and a man
4. The man in this myth comes from ___.
   - ○ a pea pod ○ water ○ clay
5. The woman in this myth comes from ___.
   - ○ a pea pod ○ water ○ clay
6. The man feels better after Raven provides ___ for him to eat.
   - ○ sheep ○ berries ○ bear
7. Raven makes the woman because ___.
   - ○ he thinks the man will be eaten by the bear
   - ○ he thinks the man will be lonely by himself
   - ○ he does not like the man he has made

Truth vs. Myth

Write the letter of the fact that Raven demonstrates by his words or actions.

_______ 1. Raven is surprised when a man comes from the pea pod, and he asks, "Who are you?"

_______ 2. Raven goes away to make berries, and it takes him four days. During this time, the man has nothing to eat.

_______ 3. Raven quickly moves out of the way after making the bear so that the bear will not eat him.

A. Raven cannot satisfy the needs of his creation quickly enough.

B. Raven does not know everything.

C. Raven is not all-powerful.

Write how the Bible truth has been twisted in the myth "The Pea-Pod Man."

4. God made man from the dust of the ground and made woman from the man's rib. ____________________

____

____

5. God gave man the responsibility to rule over and care for the world and the animals He had made. ____________________

____

____

Write the correct vocabulary word in the blank.

pool	refreshed	thrive	watercress

On a hot summer day, eating a salad can help you feel ____________. Some people think that ____________ is a tasty green to put in salads. I like to pour on the dressing and watch it ____________ among the vegetables in my bowl. Salads contain many vegetables that can help the body to ____________.

Myth Memory

Mark the correct answer.

1. The purpose of the myth *The Fire Children* is ___.
   - ○ to explain the creation of animals
   - ○ to explain the creation of children
   - ○ to explain the creation of spirit people

2. According to this myth, the earth was created by ___.
   - ○ the sky-god Nyame
   - ○ two spirit people
   - ○ the fire children

3. The spirit people enter the world by ___.
   - ○ falling through a hole in the sky
   - ○ jumping out of a basket
   - ○ flying through a trapdoor in the moon

4. The spirit people make the fire children out of ___.
   - ○ clay ○ dust ○ pea pods

5. The figures bake for different amounts of time because ___.
   - ○ the spirit people forget about them
   - ○ Nyame's visits cause the spirit people to take them out too soon or too late
   - ○ Nyame wants the children to be different colors

6. The spirit people believe that if Nyame finds out about their work he will ___.
   - ○ fear it ○ approve of it ○ disapprove of it

7. The end of the myth explains ___.
   - ○ why people of different colors live all around the world
   - ○ why Nyame was angry with the spirit people
   - ○ why the fire children were afraid of the spirit people

Truth vs. Myth

Write *G* if the statement is true of the God of the Bible. Write *N* if the statement is true of Nyame, the sky-god. Write *B* if the statement is true of both.

______ 1. created an earth

______ 2. created the man and the woman

______ 3. gave the care of the earth to others

______ 4. did not create people

______ 5. did not know about the making of children

______ 6. told the man and woman to have children

Write how the Bible truth has been twisted in the myth *The Fire Children.*

7. God created man in His own image. ______________________________

____

8. God told the man and woman to be fruitful, multiply, and fill the earth. ______________________________

____

Mark the definition of the underlined vocabulary word.

9. My tooth was throbbing with pain as I approached the door of the dentist's office.
   ○ to walk past ○ to move toward ○ to move away from
10. The island girl wore a bright hibiscus in her hair.
    ○ a tropical flower ○ an animal fur ○ a colorful feather
11. "I suspect you are hiding a frog," said Mom, looking at the lump in my coat pocket.
    ○ to explain ○ to guess with a little evidence ○ to argue
12. The trapdoor opened, and Max found himself falling through the floor.
    ○ a large front entrance ○ the trunk lid on a car ○ a small hinged opening

Retelling Creation Stories

Listen as your partner retells the creation myth of his choice. On the lines below, write down any changes he makes to the myth.

After you and your partner discuss changes made to the myths, answer these questions.

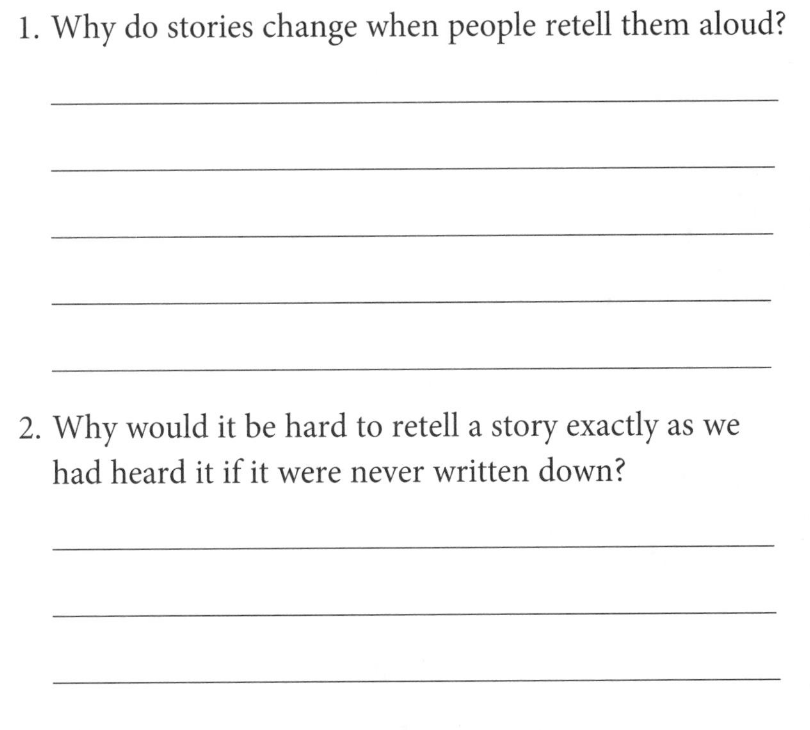

1. Why do stories change when people retell them aloud?

2. Why would it be hard to retell a story exactly as we had heard it if it were never written down?

God's Word Lasts

Read the Bible verses and answer the questions.

1. Read Luke 21:33. What does Jesus say about His words? ______________________________

2. Read 1 Peter 1:24–25. People grow old and die, just as grass and flowers cannot last. How long will the Word of God endure? ______________________________

Read the Bible verses. Write an answer to the question, using at least two verses to support your answer.

John 5:39	Romans 10:17	2 Timothy 3:16–17
John 14:21	2 Timothy 3:15	Hebrews 4:12

3. Why did God give us His written Word? ______________________________

____

____

____

____

HEAVEN AND EARTH SHALL PASS AWAY: BUT MY WORDS SHALL NOT PASS AWAY.
—LUKE 21:33

Chart It

Answer the questions.

1. What are the two main purposes of informational text? ____________________

2. What is the main purpose of the article "Can You Tell the Difference?" ____________________

____

3. Why do we organize information on two sides of a T-chart? ____________________

____

Work with a partner to choose a pair of similar animals from the article "Can You Tell the Difference?" Write an animal name at the top of each column on the T-chart. List both similar and different characteristics of each animal in the corresponding column.

•	•
•	•
•	•
•	•

Highlight the similar characteristics listed on both sides of the T-chart. Transfer all the information to the Venn diagram on Worktext page 250.

What Are the Differences?

Complete the Venn diagram using the information from Worktext page 249.

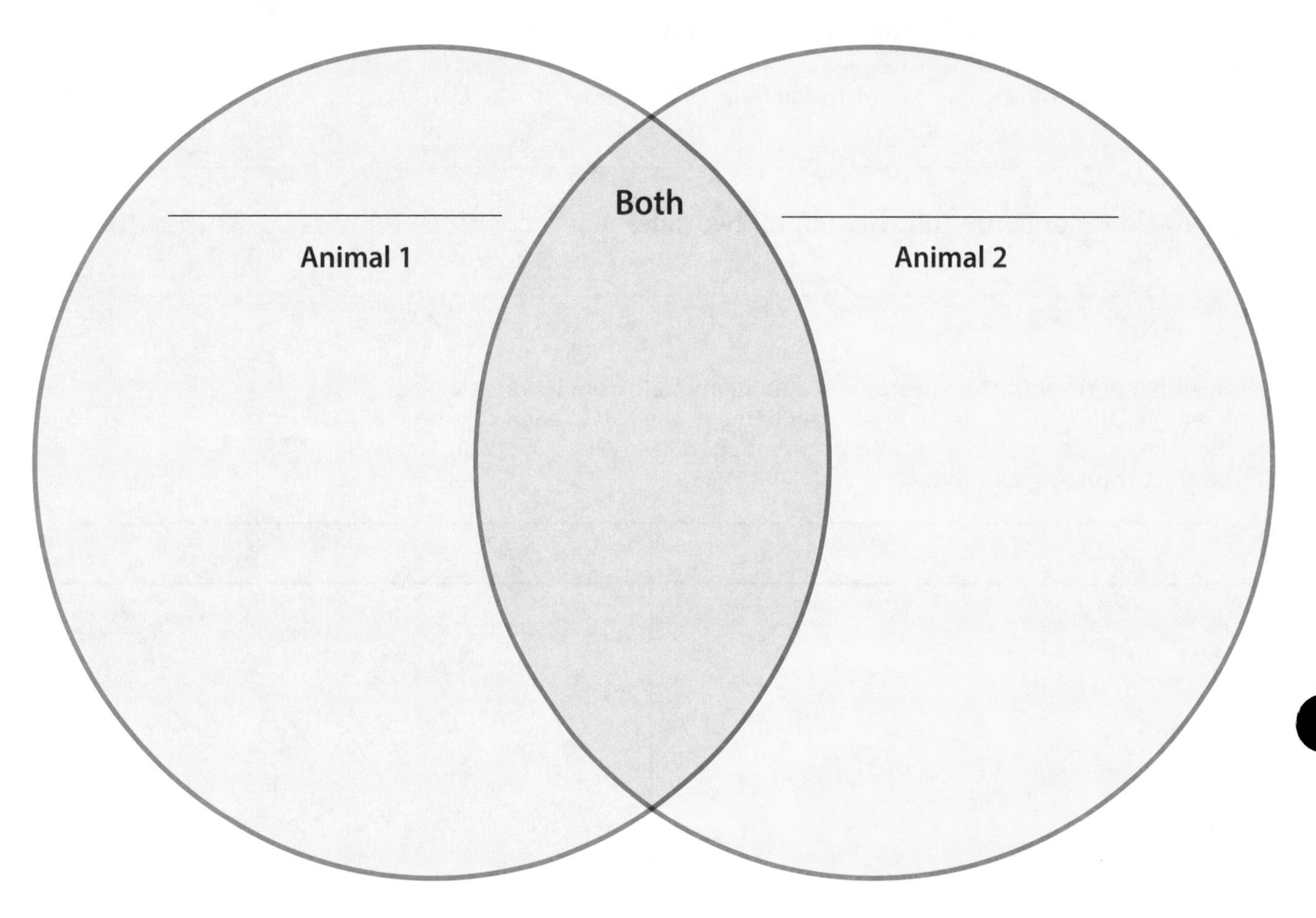

Answer the question.

Why is a Venn diagram often more helpful than a T-chart for comparing two animals?

- ○ differences are less visible
- ○ similarities are more visible
- ○ similarities are less visible

What Does It Mean?

Reread "The Rhinoceros." Mark the correct answer.

1. Which word would the poet Ogden Nash use to describe the rhinoceros?
   - ○ attractive ○ plain ○ unattractive
2. Whom does the poet credit with giving the rhinoceros its looks?
   - ○ God ○ Nature ○ its parents
3. What word is *prepoceros* a misspelling of?
   - ○ precision ○ precipitous ○ preposterous
4. What is the meaning of the misspelled word?
   - ○ scientific ○ silly ○ intelligent
5. What is the mood of this poem?
   - ○ humorous ○ sorrowful ○ serious
6. What question does the poet create in your mind?
   - ○ What does the rhinoceros enjoy feasting on?
   - ○ Why does the rhinoceros appear so peculiar?
   - ○ Where is the rhinoceros's dwelling place?
7. What does the poet's use of "Nature" tell you about his worldview?
   - ○ He believes the world was created in six days.

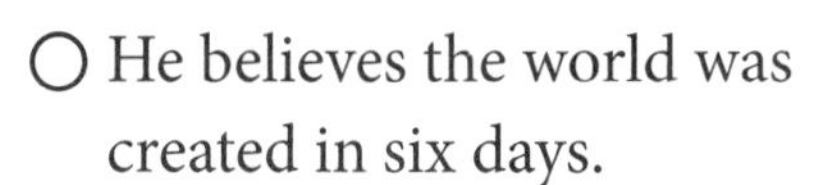

   - ○ He believes the truth of the Bible.
   - ○ He believes in a creator other than God.

Word Play

Word play is using words in a clever way that often creates humor.

> The bumble and the honey bee—
> Their names do suit them well;
> For the "humble" and the "bunny" bee
> Would not be half as swell!

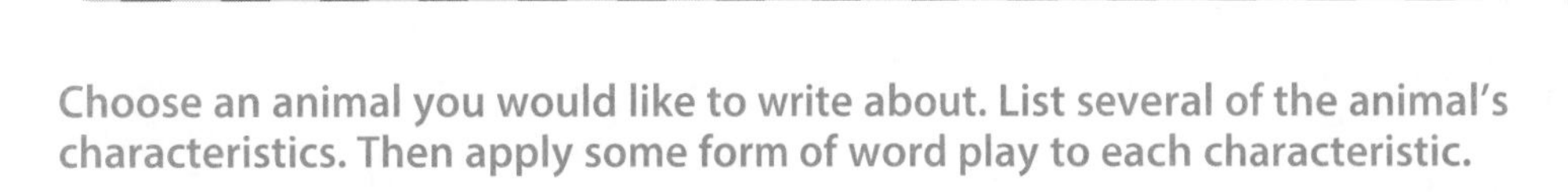

Choose an animal you would like to write about. List several of the animal's characteristics. Then apply some form of word play to each characteristic.

Animal: ____________________	
Characteristic	**Word play (misspelling, double meaning, exaggeration)**
____________	________________________________
____________	________________________________
____________	________________________________
____________	________________________________

Use the word play to help you write your own four-line poem.

____

____

____

____

Rhino vs. Hippo

Research to find characteristics of a rhinoceros and a hippopotamus. List several characteristics to complete the T-chart. Include at least one similar characteristic.

Rhinoceros	Hippopotamus
•	•
•	•
•	•
•	•
•	•

Highlight the similar characteristics listed on both sides of the T-chart. Answer the questions. Use the information to write a one-paragraph article on Worktext page 254.

1. What do you want the reader to learn about the rhinoceros and hippopotamus?

2. Do you hope to persuade the reader of something?

Inform Others

Write a one-paragraph article to compare and contrast the rhinoceros and the hippopotamus. Make up a catchy title that will cause others to want to read the article. Begin with a topic sentence, followed by supporting details and ending with a restatement of the purpose for the paragraph.

Title

Draw or attach a picture that supports the information in your paragraph.

Cultural Variations

Based on your research, mark all answers that are correct.

1. "The Soup Stone" is a folktale that has been told in the country of ___.
   - ○ Germany
   - ○ France
   - ○ England
2. Depending on the culture, the soup in the folktale has been made using ___.
   - ○ an axe
   - ○ a kite
   - ○ a button
3. Depending on the culture, the main character in the folktale has been ___.
   - ○ a king
   - ○ a soldier
   - ○ a monk

Write the answer.

4. Why are there many variations of this folktale? ______________________________

____

____

Match the element of the play with the description.

______ 5. setting
______ 6. stage direction
______ 7. characters

A. 1st Housewife, Traveler, Tildy
B. a street in a small village
C. two dogs begin to bark

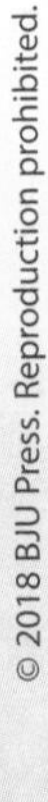

Match the stage direction with the definition.

______ 8. at rise
______ 9. enter
______ 10. offstage
______ 11. curtain
______ 12. exit

A. character dialogue happening away from the stage
B. describes what is on the stage when the play begins
C. direction to leave the stage
D. direction to come onto the stage
E. direction at the end of a scene, act, or play

Define It!

Mark the word or phrase that means the same as the bold word.

1. The girl apologized to her friend for speaking **tartly** to him.

   ○ sharply ○ softly ○ kindly

2. The man's **trousers** were covered with white paint after he sat on the park bench.

   ○ running shoes ○ pants ○ shirt sleeves

3. "I **appreciate** all the kind things you did for me while I was sick," said the old lady.

   ○ am tired of ○ am fearful of ○ am grateful for

4. The neighbor **vigorously** shook the locked door of the burning house after hearing cries for help.

   ○ gently ○ weakly ○ forcefully

5. The boy **stalked** home after his team lost the game by one point.

   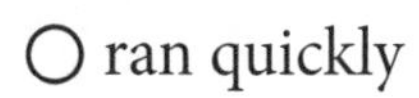
   ○ ran quickly

   ○ walked angrily

   ○ tiptoed

6. The man **furiously** tackled the thief and held him until the police arrived.

   ○ angrily

   ○ happily

   ○ willingly

Motives and Actions

Write each letter in the correct boxes. Letters may be used more than once.

Main characters	Character's motivation (A, B, C)	Character's actions (D, E, F)	Scripture that applies to the character (G, H, I)
Traveler			
Tildy			
John			

A. wants something for nothing
B. generous
C. hungry
D. lets a stranger into home
E. uses trickery to get a free meal
F. helps to gather ingredients
G. 2 Thessalonians 3:10
H. Proverbs 12:22
I. Deuteronomy 15:11

Read the paragraph. Answer the questions.

Tilly shrieked and fainted after taking one look at the huge snake sunning itself on home plate. Jane haughtily took charge of the situation. Critically, she looked at the markings on the snake and the shape of its eyes. Jane was sure the snake was not poisonous. She searched intently for a strong stick. When she found one, she carefully lifted the snake off home plate. Jane placed the sleepy reptile on a large rock near right field. The snake indifferently curled up, resuming its nap. Used to Tilly's fainting spells, Jane passed a small tube under Tilly's nose. The strong aroma of smelling salts worked to awaken Tilly. Now the camp's championship ball game could begin.

______ 1. Which word means "smell"?

______ 2. Which word means "proudly"?

______ 3. Which word means "going back to"?

______ 4. Which word means "carefully analyzing"?

______ 5. Which word means "closely with attention"?

______ 6. Which word means "not interested one way or the other"?

Pre-performance Brainstorming

Brainstorm to complete the graphic organizers with lists of necessary scenery and props.

Brainstorm to create a list of post-play discussion questions to evaluate Traveler's words and actions from a biblical worldview.

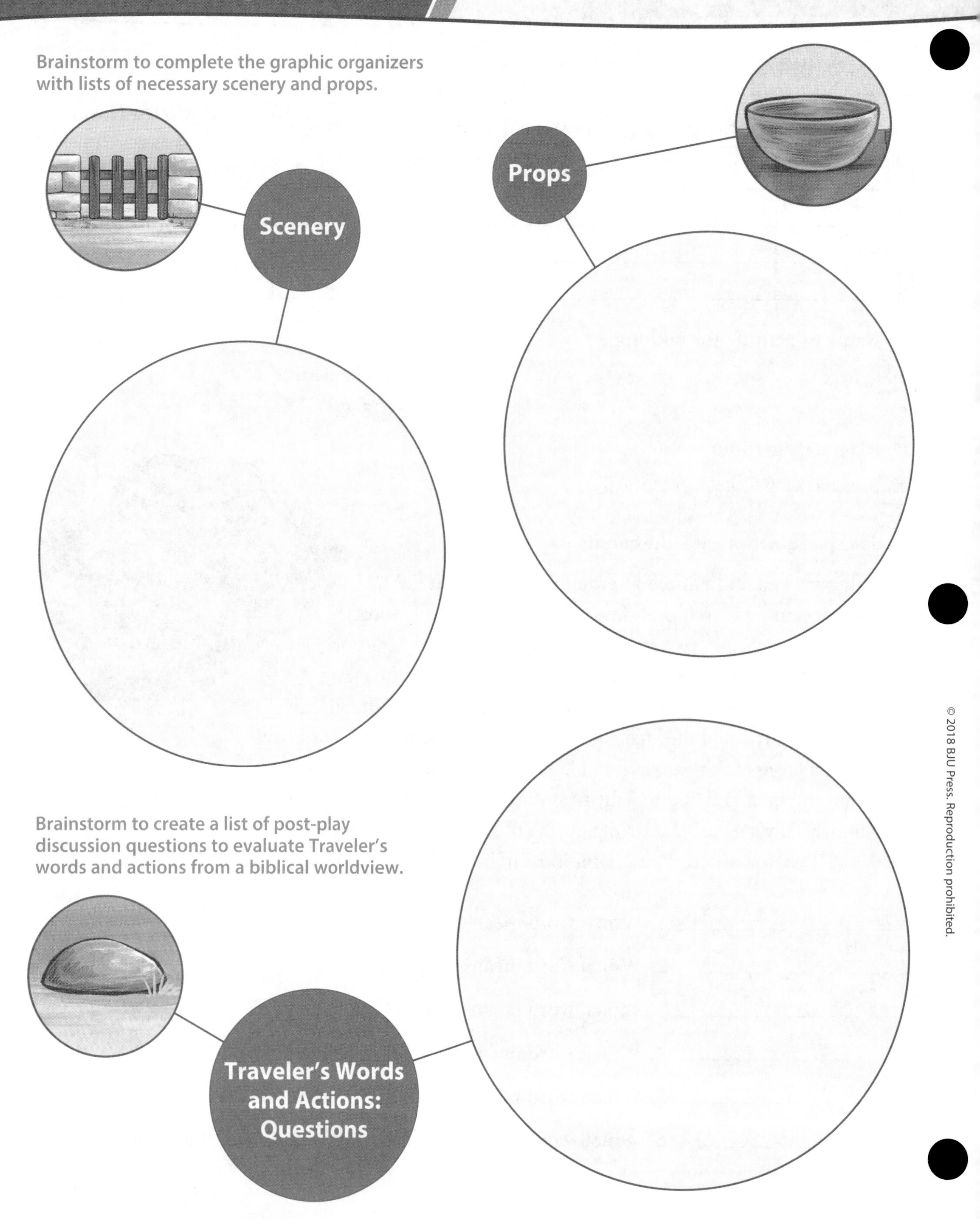

Write the answers.

1. How long does it take to prepare the ingredients for this Stone Soup recipe? ____________

2. How many people does this recipe serve? ____________

3. List six different ingredients needed to make this recipe.

4. How much ground thyme does the recipe call for? ____________

5. What should the soup be cooked in? ____________

6. How long does it take for the soup to cook? ____________

7. How will you know when the soup is done? ____________

8. What did you like about the soup recipe? ____________

9. What did you *not* like about the soup recipe? ____________

10. What vegetables would you add to or remove from this recipe to suit *your* taste?

My Very Own Recipe

Create your own recipe for a sandwich. List all ingredients. Write out step-by-step directions for making your one-of-a-kind sandwich.

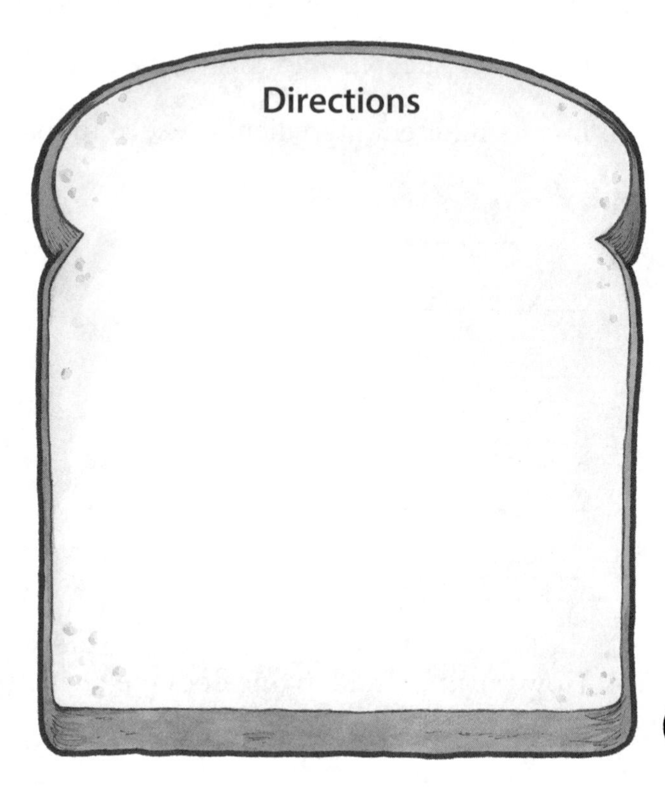

Match the vocabulary word with its definition.

_______ 1. dice

 2. shred

_______ 3. stalk

_______ 4. yield

A. the stem of a plant

B. the number of servings

C. to cut into long narrow strips

D. to cut into small cubes

What an Experience!

Complete the statements about poetry.

Poetry expresses ____________ and ____________, often in only a few lines. A free verse poem does not have a regular pattern of ____________ and ____________.

Summarize what is being described in each stanza of "Firefly."

Stanza 1
Stanza 2
Stanza 3

Identify the senses that each stanza appeals to.

Stanza 1
Stanza 2
Stanza 3

Write your answer.

After reading this poem, what ideas or feelings do you have about the firefly, which God created? ____________

This Means the Same as That

Looking at how a word is used in a sentence can help you decide the meaning of that word.

Match the bold vocabulary word with its definition. Use the Glossary as needed.

A. a group of stars	C. cleverly	E. foreign
B. bitter	D. a large cave	F. mysterious

_______ 1. The **alien** landscape in Alaska looked nothing like Mac's hometown in Kansas.

_______ 2. The **astringent** odor in the lab made Carrie cover her nose and run out of the room.

_______ 3. Leigh and Melanie could hear their voices echo as they called to one another in the dark **cavern**.

_______ 4. The blinking **constellation** in the night sky caused Candace to think of the summer fun of catching fireflies.

_______ 5. The **enigmatic** man stood in the shadow of the building as he spied on the bank.

_______ 6. Marvin moved **slyly** through the woods to avoid being captured by the other team.

Sense the Image

Sensory words help us see, feel, smell, taste, and hear.

Identify the sensory words or phrases in "Firefly."

See	Feel	Smell

Think of a topic such as a birthday, a ball game, a vacation, or Christmas. Create a list of sensory words about your topic. List words under all five senses.

Topic: ____________________

See	Feel	Smell	Taste	Hear

The Way I See It

Imagery is the use of words to create a picture in our minds. Imagery appeals to our senses.

Write a brief description of your topic or of a personal experience that is related to your topic. Use your list of sensory words from the previous page.

Create an illustration of the topic or experience that you wrote about.

Match the type of poetry with the correct poem. One word will not be used.

A. acrostic	B. haiku	C. limerick	D. palindrome

_______ 1. There once was a boy named Bob
Who loved to eat corn on the cob.
He ate and he ate
Till he emptied his plate,
And his mother remarked, "Good job!"

_______ 2. A long rope with scales
Stretches in the bright sun and
Flashes a forked tongue.

_______ 3. Picking his spot carefully, the cat jumps
Up on the windowsill and lies down to
Rest; deep under his fluff, he
Rumbles in drowsy happiness.

Write your answers about "Hornbill's Hot Day."

4. Who is speaking in the poem? _______________
5. What is the theme of the poem? _______________
6. Explain how the shape of the poem shows the topic. _______________
7. How do the acrostics and palindromes strengthen the theme of the poem? _______________

My Acrostic

Complete the acrostic to describe a frog.

F____________________

R____________________

O____________________

G____________________

Write the word that completes the sentence.

marveled	scarlet	splendid	squawk	utter	wattle

1. John's face turned ____________ when he spilled his drink all over his teacher's shoes.
2. As we drove away from the city lights, we ____________ at how brightly the stars sparkled.
3. The rooster looked silly as it ran across the yard with its red ____________ swinging back and forth.
4. We stopped our hike to admire the ____________ view of the waterfall pouring over the cliff.
5. I was so surprised by the booming thunder that I could not ____________ one word!
6. When we heard a loud ____________ in the hen house, we wondered whether the coyote had come back.

Walled In

Write *T* if the statement is true of informational text features. Write *F* if the statement is false. Rewrite the underlined part to make it a true statement.

_______ 1. A section title helps explain a photograph. _______________

_______ 2. A sidebar gives additional information that helps the reader understand the main text of the article. _______________

_______ 3. Each section has a main idea that is supported by details throughout the section. _______________

_______ 4. Chapter titles are usually not very important to the main idea. _______________

Write the answers.

5. Write a summary of the main idea of Chapter 1. _______________

6. How is the information in Chapter 1 related to the title, "Walled In"? _______________

Mark all the details that support the main idea of Chapter 1.

- ○ Hornbills live in the rainforests and grasslands of Asia and Africa.
- ○ A mother hornbill finds a hole in a tree trunk to start preparing her nest.
- ○ A tropical rainforest is humid and warm all the time.
- ○ Hornbills can be small or large.
- ○ The rainforest hornbills live in the canopy.
- ○ A mother hornbill stays sealed in her nest for a few months.
- ○ The largest temperate rainforests are located in the Pacific Northwest, Alaska, and Canada.

What a Beak!

Refer to Student Text pages 653–54. Write *MI* beside the statement that is the main idea of Chapter 2. Write *SD* beside the supporting details for the main idea.

_______ Hornbills live in the rainforest canopy.

_______ Different kinds of hornbills have different shapes and sizes of casques.

_______ The hornbill has an interesting appearance.

_______ A mother hornbill stays inside her nest for several months.

_______ A hornbill's "eyelashes" are made of thin feathers that protect their eyes.

_______ A rainforest can provide medicine, wood, coffee, cocoa, spices, and fruit.

_______ Hornbills use their beaks to rub yellow or orange oil on their feathers.

Mark the synonym of the underlined vocabulary word.

1. The pirate reached into the cavity of the old tree to get the treasure map he had hidden there weeks before.

   ○ nest ○ hole ○ curve

2. After splashing in the pond, the ducks preened their feathers with their beaks.

   ○ cleaned ○ pulled ○ plucked

3. Eating twenty hot dogs would be impressive—and also sickening!

   ○ amazing ○ disgusting ○ fun

4. When our dog ran away, we plastered our neighborhood with pictures so that people could help us look for him.

   ○ sprinkled ○ covered ○ showered

5. An elephant and a hummingbird are not the same species of animal.

   ○ color ○ size ○ type

Filling the Bill

Refer to Student Text page 655. Complete the graphic organizer using your own words to summarize.

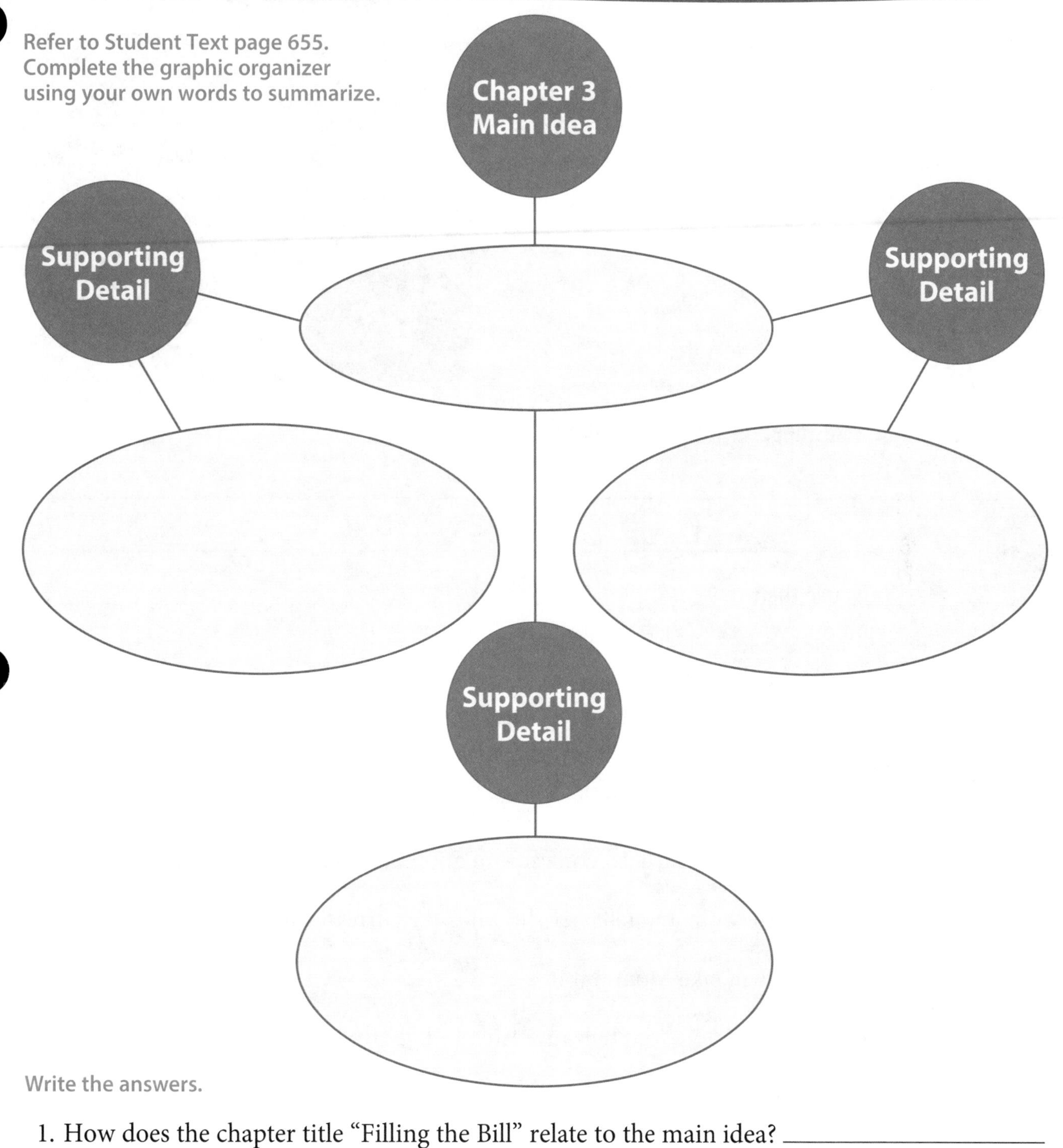

Write the answers.

1. How does the chapter title "Filling the Bill" relate to the main idea? ______________________

____

2. Explain how hornbills help the rainforest. ______________________

____

____

The Hornbill's Life

Write an *X* beside the correct answer.

Another title for Chapter 4, "The Hornbill's Life," might be ___.

_______ "The Hornbill's Food"

_______ "The Hornbill Family"

_______ "Where the Hornbill Lives"

_______ "Hornbill Feathers and Beak"

Write three details that support the chapter title "The Hornbill's Life."

____

____

____

Complete the paragraph with the vocabulary words.

courts	filthy	flirts	sprout	victor

On Valentine's Day, it seems as if Dad comes from another species! In the morning, he _______________ with Mom and tells her she will get a surprise later in the day. Then, he says there is no way he will take Mom out in a _______________ car, so he washes it in the afternoon before their date. Mom tells my sister and me the story of how she and Dad met. Mom says that love between two people can _______________ as they get to know each other. Mom laughs when we give her strange looks at this idea. In the evening, Dad _______________ Mom by bringing her chocolate and roses. Mom is so happy that she gives him a hug. Dad grins as though he were the _______________ of a championship football game!

Hornbill

Write the answer.

What is the main idea of Chapter 5? ______________________________

Write an *X* beside each statement that supports the main idea of Chapter 5.

_______ Hornbill pairs stay together for the rest of their lives.

_______ Hornbills depend on the rainforest for food and safe nesting places.

_______ A rainforest is an ecosystem that receives a large amount of rain each year.

_______ People sometimes kill hornbills in order to sell their beaks and casques for a lot of money.

_______ The hornbills lose their homes when the rainforest is cut down by loggers and farmers.

_______ Hornbills live in Africa and Asia and eat fruit, insects, and small reptiles.

_______ Scientists are teaching people how they can protect the hornbills.

Mark each statement that shows the author's purpose in writing *Hornbill.*

○ to inform the reader about how a hornbill lives and behaves

○ to persuade the reader that hornbills need to be protected and cared for

○ to entertain the reader with a description of hornbill tricks

○ to persuade the reader that the rainforests need to be cared for so that hornbills can continue living

○ to create suspense as the reader learns about hornbills

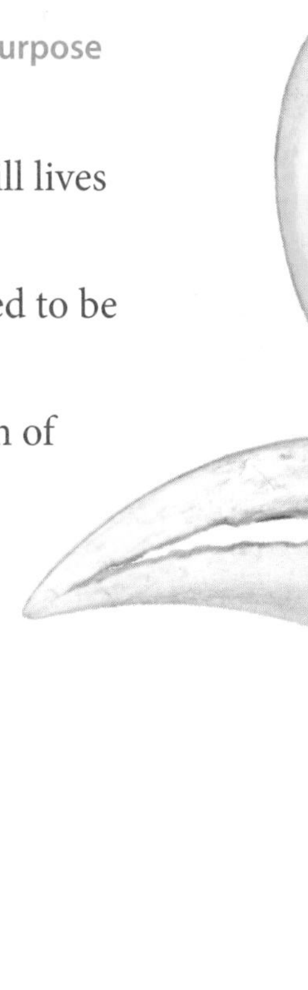

Read the paragraph. Mark the answers.

Spring is the best season! After a long winter, it is exciting to see bits of fresh green on the brown trees. Daffodils poking up through the ground offer hope that winter is over and that warmer days are coming. The spring sky is a happy blue with friendly clouds that almost seem to smile as they drift by. Spring is full of new life in the bright blooms of early flowers and the cheeping of baby birds. Hurry and come, Spring, because you are the best season of all!

1. What is the main idea of the paragraph?
   - ○ Daffodils poking up through the ground offer hope that winter is over.
   - ○ Spring is the best season!
2. The author's purpose is ___.
   - ○ to inform the reader with facts about nature in the spring
   - ○ to persuade the reader that spring is the best season

Write the letter of the vocabulary word that completes each sentence. Some words will not be used.

A. data	B. destruction	C. poacher	D. recover	E. splendid	F. threat

_______ 3. The dark clouds were a ___ to our soccer game because the coach will not let us play if there is thunder and lightning.

_______ 4. It took my grandpa a few months to ___ from his knee surgery.

_______ 5. Mom lost all the ___ in her document because she forgot to save her work as she typed.

_______ 6. A tornado can cause terrible ___ by blowing over houses, trees, and cars.

Write a sentence using the word *uncertain*.

7. ____

____

Stewardship of Creation

Genesis 2:15

And the Lord God took the man, and put him into the garden of Eden to dress it and to keep it.

Write the answer.

1. What is a "steward"? ____________________

____

2. Explain what it means that people are "stewards" of God's creation. ____________________

____

Write *S* beside each statement that shows good stewardship.

_______ Sarah sat on a park bench eating a candy bar. When she finished eating, she threw the wrapper on the ground and ran off to play with her friends.

_______ Before we left the house, Dad turned off all the lights and the air conditioning. He also made sure all of the hoses in the garden were turned off.

_______ Our school planted flowers and a few small trees along the new sidewalk.

_______ The mechanic dumped several buckets of old oil into the lake near his shop.

_______ Kate and her brother are collecting aluminum cans from their neighbors. They will take them to their city's recycling center at the end of the month.

_______ Paul gathered some rocks and threw them at a bird's nest for target practice. The eggs fell to the ground and broke. He threw a rock at the mother bird as she flew around the broken eggs.

_______ Grandma makes pretty purses out of old pairs of jeans. She gives them as presents to her friends.

Stewardship in Action

Research an idea for a class project that shows good stewardship of creation. This idea may include ways to help or care for plants or animals or ways to use less of a natural resource. Your project may also involve reusing or recycling. Write the information below as you conduct your research.

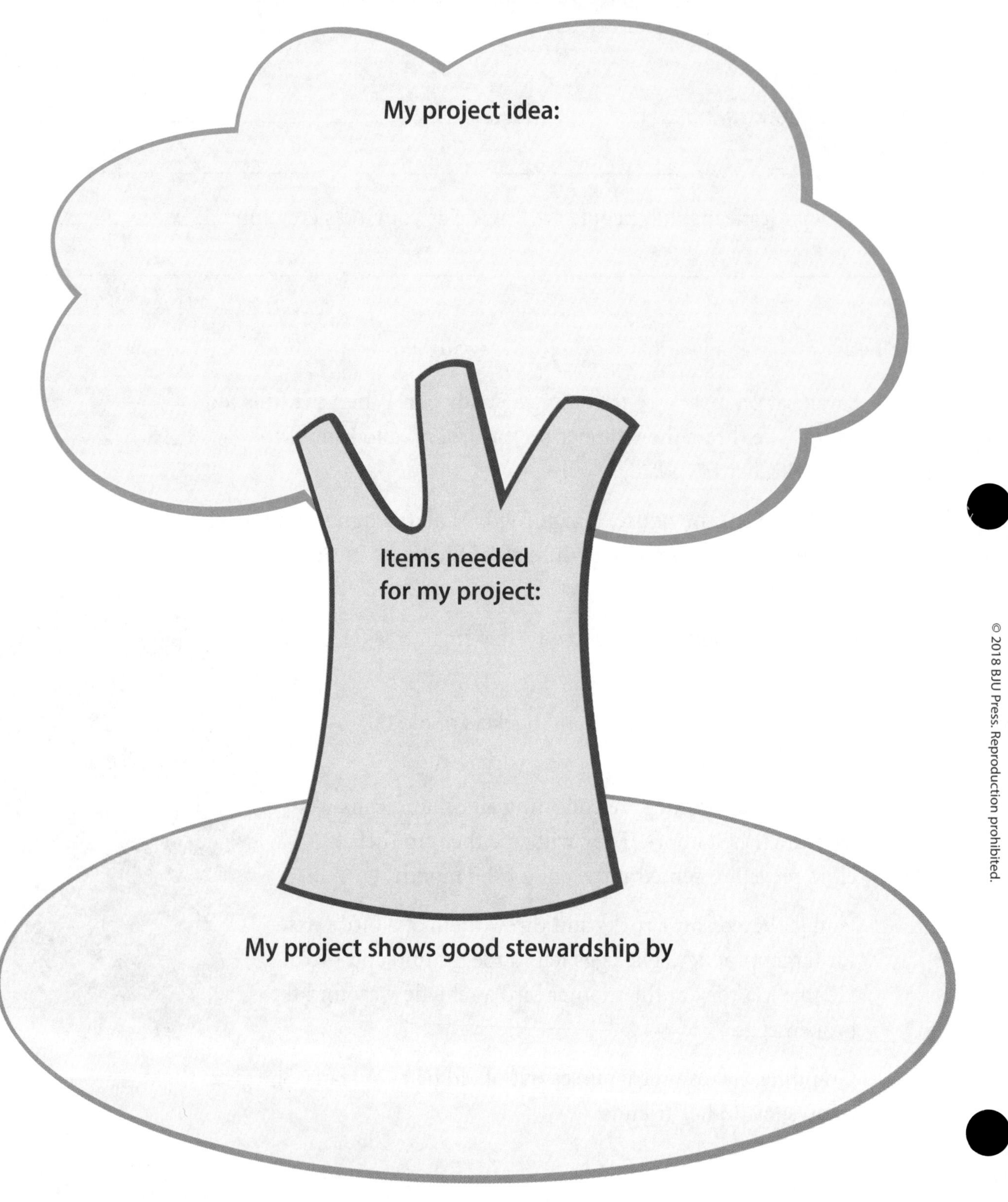

A Dragon at Heart

Write the answers.

1. What is the problem in the story? ______________________________

____

2. What do these statements tell you about Eustace's character before he became a dragon?

"Eustace's character had been rather improved by becoming a dragon. He was anxious to help." ______________________________

"The pleasure (quite new to him) of being liked and, still more, of liking other people, was what kept Eustace from despair." ______________________________

____

3. Write a sentence about the story's setting. ______________________________

____

Match each character with the statement that best applies to him.

_______ 4. Eustace

_______ 5. Reepicheep

_______ 6. Edmund

_______ 7. The lion

A. He listens patiently because he senses that another character has an important story to tell.

B. He is surrounded by light and has a commanding presence; he must be obeyed.

C. He is described as "noble" because of his kind, comforting care toward someone who has despised him in the past.

D. He is humbled because he is beginning to understand the depth of his selfishness.

Scaly Skin

Mark the correct answer.

1. When Eustace first sees the lion, he feels ___.

   ○ happy ○ fearful ○ angry

2. The lion leads Eustace to a ___.

   ○ beach ○ campfire ○ well

3. Eustace wants to get into the water to ___.

   ○ ease his leg pain ○ enjoy a swim ○ hide from the lion

4. When the lion tells Eustace to undress himself, he is telling Eustace to ___.

   ○ remove his clothes ○ remove his skin ○ remove the bracelet

5. Eustace does not complete the lion's order because ___.

   ○ he does not want to obey the lion

   ○ he cannot reach deep enough beneath his layers of skin

   ○ he does not try hard enough

Write the word that best completes each sentence.

cast	ghastly	humane	nuisance	obstinate	scales

6. When I opened my brother's door, the ____________________ sight of a snakeskin greeted me, and I screamed.

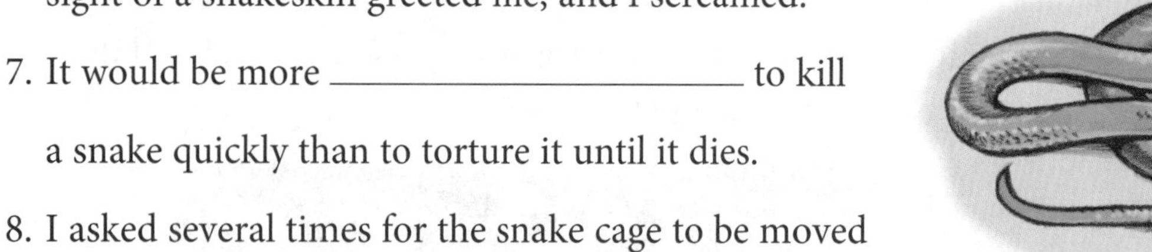

7. It would be more ____________________ to kill a snake quickly than to torture it until it dies.

8. I asked several times for the snake cage to be moved outside, but my ____________________ brother always refused.

9. My brother and his snakes became such a ____________________ that I asked Mom and Dad whether I could move into the attic.

10. Do eels ____________________ their skins several times a year as snakes do?

11. No, most eels have slimy skin with no ____________________ to shed.

"Un-dragoned"

Mark all the correct answers for each question.

1. Why does Eustace let Aslan remove his skin even though he is afraid of the lion's claws?
   - ○ He is desperate to have the skin taken off.
   - ○ He knows he cannot remove the skin himself.
   - ○ He thinks the claws will not really hurt him.

2. How is Eustace able to bear the peeling off of his skin by Aslan?
   - ○ He does not feel any pain.
   - ○ He is pleased that the deep layers of his skin are finally coming off.
   - ○ He is relieved that he will no longer have to be a dragon.

3. Why does Eustace refer to his swim in the well as "perfectly delicious"?
   - ○ It is enjoyable being a boy again and having arms to splash with in the water.
   - ○ He sees that his arms have become strong and muscular.
   - ○ His pain has gone away because the bracelet is no longer tight on his arm.

4. What does Aslan do for Eustace after his swim in the well?
   - ○ He gives him the dragon skin to keep.
   - ○ He gives him new clothes.
   - ○ He puts him back near his friends.

5. What character traits of Aslan are shown in this event?
   - ○ He is powerful enough to change people who cannot change themselves.
   - ○ He has a commanding presence; he must be feared and obeyed.
   - ○ He is too merciful to leave people in the miserable condition in which he meets them.

6. Why do the events on Dragon Island end with the "curious fate" of the bracelet?
   - ○ The ending reminds us that we do not need to carry our greed and selfishness with us.
   - ○ The ending makes us sad that no one else will wear the bracelet.
   - ○ The ending makes us happy that the bracelet will never again tempt anyone to put it on.

Story Symbols

Read each Scripture passage. Answer the questions.

1. While trapped in the dragon skin, Eustace has to be a dragon. He cannot get rid of his bat-like wings and cruel claws. He has to kill animals for food. He cannot speak. Fire and smoke come out when he breathes. Read Ephesians 2:1–3 and Romans 8:6–7. What do you think the dragon skin represents? ______________________
2. Only Aslan is able to tear the dragon skin off Eustace. Eustace's own efforts to tear it off do not work because it is more than just a few layers of skin on the outside. Aslan has to reach deep inside to completely remove the dragon skin from Eustace. Read Romans 6:6–7, 11–12 and Ephesians 2:8–9. Whom does Aslan represent? ______________________
   What has Jesus done for the Christian? ______________________
   ____
3. Eustace still has "relapses," even after the dragon skin is removed. Read 2 Corinthians 5:17 and Ephesians 4:20–24. What is true about a Christian's struggle with sin and his new nature? ______________________
   ____

Mark the correct answer. Use the Glossary as needed.

4. I thought I was over the flu, but I had a <u>relapse</u> and missed school again today.
   - ○ return of a condition
   - ○ accidental injury
   - ○ change to better health
5. I hope my symptoms will <u>vanish</u> by next week.
   ○ come back ○ increase ○ disappear
6. I would really like to have my health <u>restored</u> so that I can go on the field trip.
   ○ brought back ○ interrupted ○ broken

Write the correct answers in the blanks.

Story Structure: *The Voyage of the* Dawn Treader

	Fantasy	Real Christian experience
Characters	______________ Reepicheep and Edmund Aslan	A person in need of salvation Christian friends ______________
Setting	______________ ______________	The real world
Problem	______________ ______________ ______________ ______________	A person's sin places him in a miserable condition that he cannot change. The person is controlled by his sinful nature, or his flesh.
Solution	Only Aslan is able to remove Eustace's dragon skin.	______________ ______________ ______________ ______________

The Voyage of the *Dawn Treader*

Mark all the correct answers for each question.

1. Which of the following statements are true of fantasy?
   - ○ Fantasy is a story that could not happen in real life.
   - ○ Fantasy never has any similarities to real life.
   - ○ Fantasy may remind us of real life experiences.

2. C. S. Lewis weaves Christian themes into fantasy because ___.
   - ○ fantasy can help us understand real Christian experience
   - ○ fantasy can picture spiritual truth
   - ○ fantasy and the Bible always teach the same things

3. Which statement best expresses the theme of the story of Eustace and the dragon skin from *The Voyage of the* Dawn Treader?
   - ○ Dragons may be powerful, but we can defeat them if we try as hard as we can.
   - ○ Only Jesus can remove the "dragon skin" of sin and make a person new and free.
   - ○ We must remove our own "dragon skin" of sin without help from anyone.

Write the answer.

4. How effective was this story in helping you understand spiritual truth? Write something that the story made you realize about Jesus or about yourself. ______________________

____

____

____

____

____

____

____

____

Plot and Symbols

Complete the graphic organizer to summarize the plot of this selection from *The Voyage of the* Dawn Treader. Remember to tell about the problem and the solution.

Beginning	
Middle	
End	

Write the meaning of each symbol in the story.

1. The dragon skin represents ____________________.
2. The bracelet represents ____________________.
3. Aslan represents ____________________.

Two Versions of the Story

Using the Venn diagram, compare and contrast the adaptation you watched or heard with C. S. Lewis's original story in your Student Text.

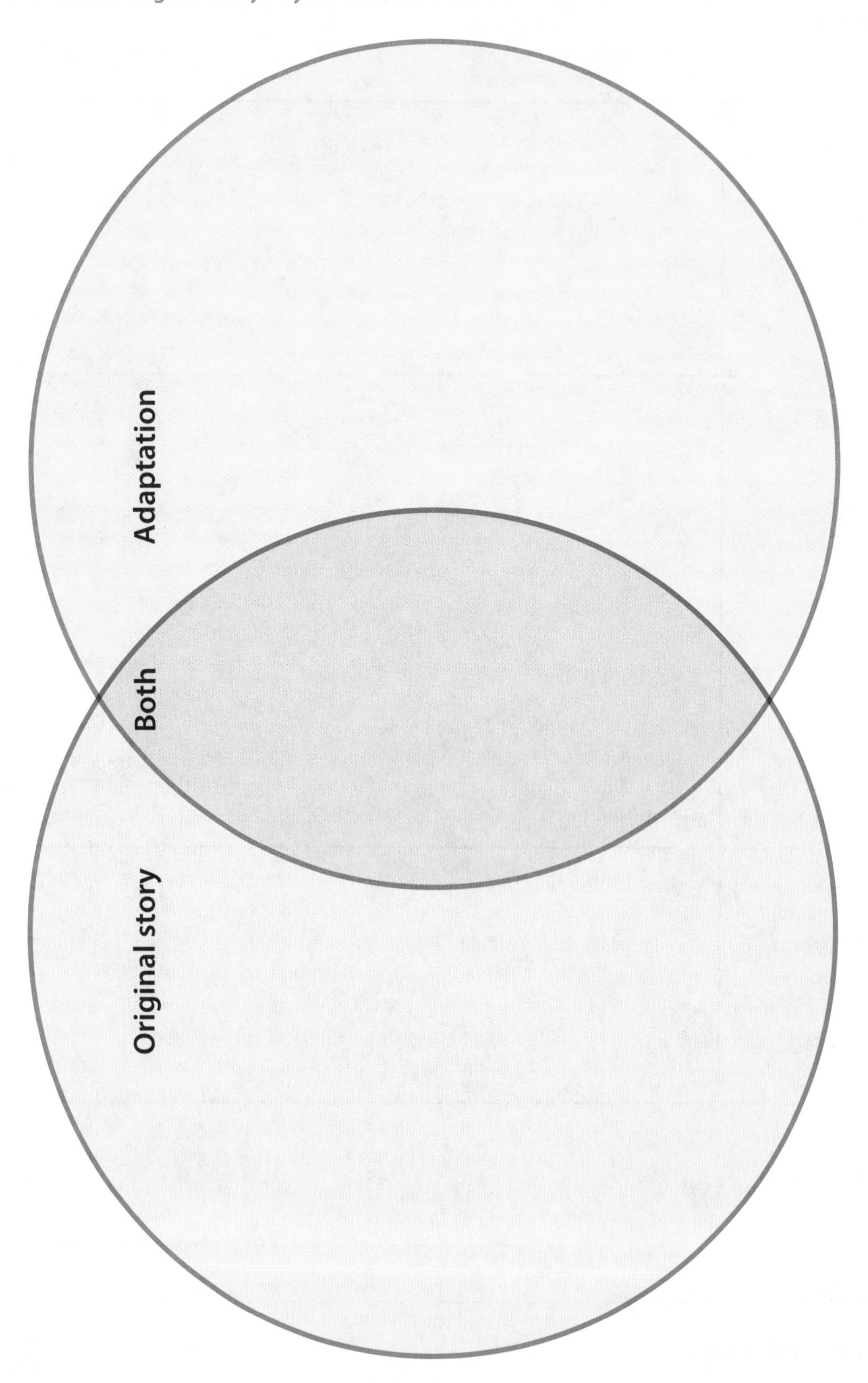

Planning My Paragraph

____

List two Bible verses or passages that you would like to use to discuss the story of Eustace, Aslan, and the dragon skin.

1. ______________________________

2. ______________________________

Romans 8:6–7	Ephesians 2:1–3
Romans 6:6–7	Ephesians 2:8–9
Romans 6:11–12	Ephesians 4:20–24
2 Corinthians 5:17	

Use the graphic organizer to plan your persuasive paragraph. Remember to use the Bible passages as you write your reasons and supporting details.

Topic sentence: I believe ______________________________

represents biblical truth better than ______________________________.

Reason 1:

Reason 2:

Supporting detail:

Supporting detail:

Supporting detail:

Supporting detail:

My Persuasive Paragraph

Choose one reason with its supporting details to develop into a paragraph. Write your paragraph on the lines below. Remember to begin with the topic sentence.

There Is No Frigate like a Book

Mark the correct answer.

1. In "There Is No Frigate like a Book," the poet Emily Dickinson compares reading to what?
   - ○ a difficult job
   - ○ a foot race
   - ○ an adventurous journey
2. Which image is *not* used to describe reading?
   - ○ riding in a chariot
   - ○ flying on a plane
   - ○ sailing on a ship
3. How is a book related to a ship in the poem?
   - ○ takes us to faraway lands
   - ○ travels in water
   - ○ makes us seasick
4. How is poetry related to a horse in the poem?
   - ○ is written in lines
   - ○ has a prancing rhythm
   - ○ pulls heavy loads
5. What does the phrase "without oppress of Toll" mean?
   - ○ without having to pay
   - ○ without having to work
   - ○ without any enjoyment

Write the answer.

6. What is the theme of the poem? State the theme in your own words. ______________________

____

7. How do the images in the poem remind you of a journey? ______________________

____

There Is No Frigate like a Book

What books or selections from your reading this year took you on a journey of your imagination? Write the titles on the sails.

Mark the correct answer. The first two vocabulary words can be found in the Glossary.

8. I thought the diamond necklace was <u>phony</u> because I had never seen blue diamonds.
   ○ fake ○ expensive ○ shiny
9. A peninsula is a <u>projection</u> of land that stretches into the ocean.
   ○ large area ○ extended part ○ coastal plain
10. The bridge provided a <u>traverse</u> over the river.
    ○ cover ○ path ○ shipment
11. We have to pay a <u>toll</u> to drive on this section of the highway.
    ○ booth ○ dollar bill ○ fee
12. My mother is too <u>frugal</u> to buy expensive clothes.
    ○ thrifty ○ foolish ○ fashionable